ANATOMY OF THE LIGHTHOUSE

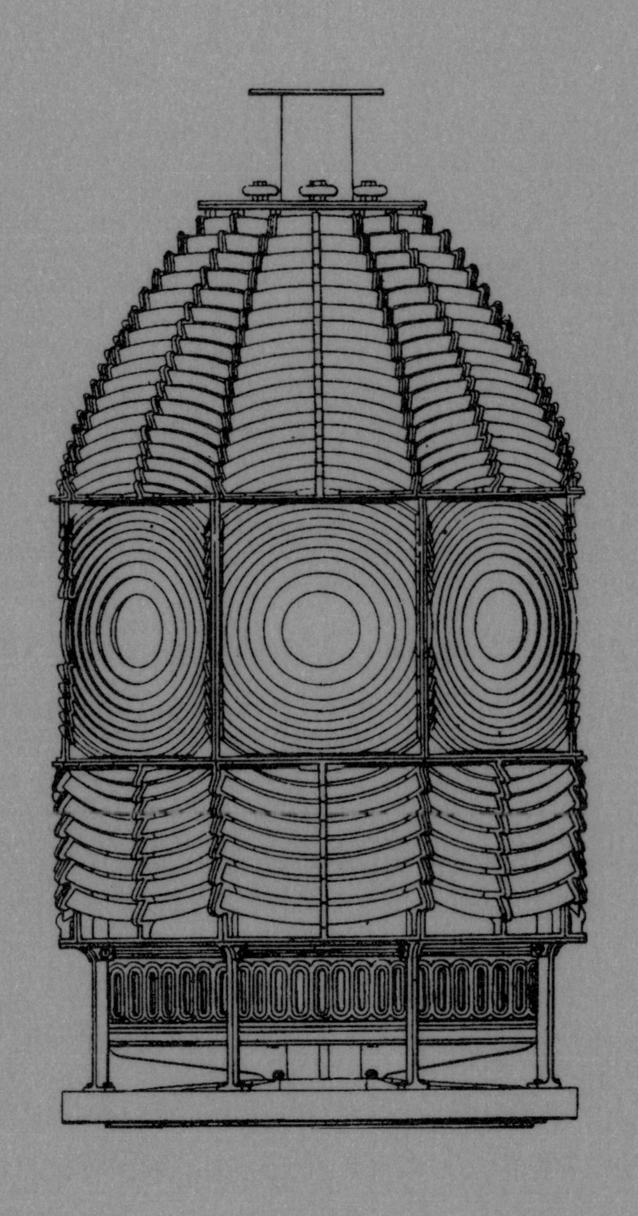

ANATOMY OF THE LIGHTHOUSE

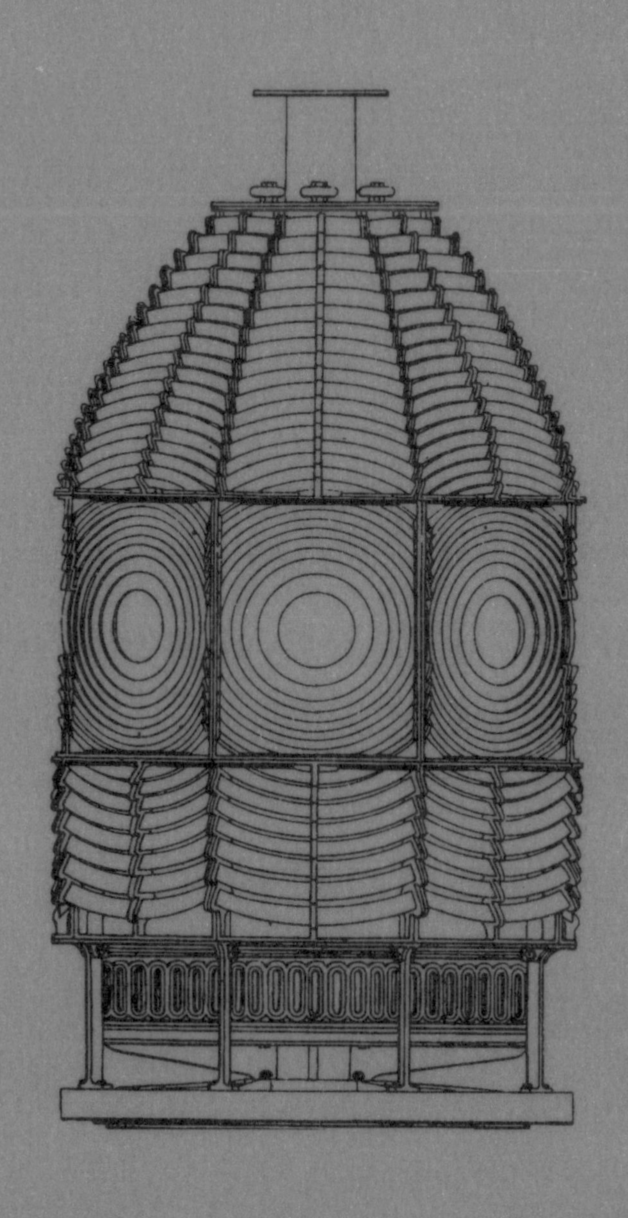

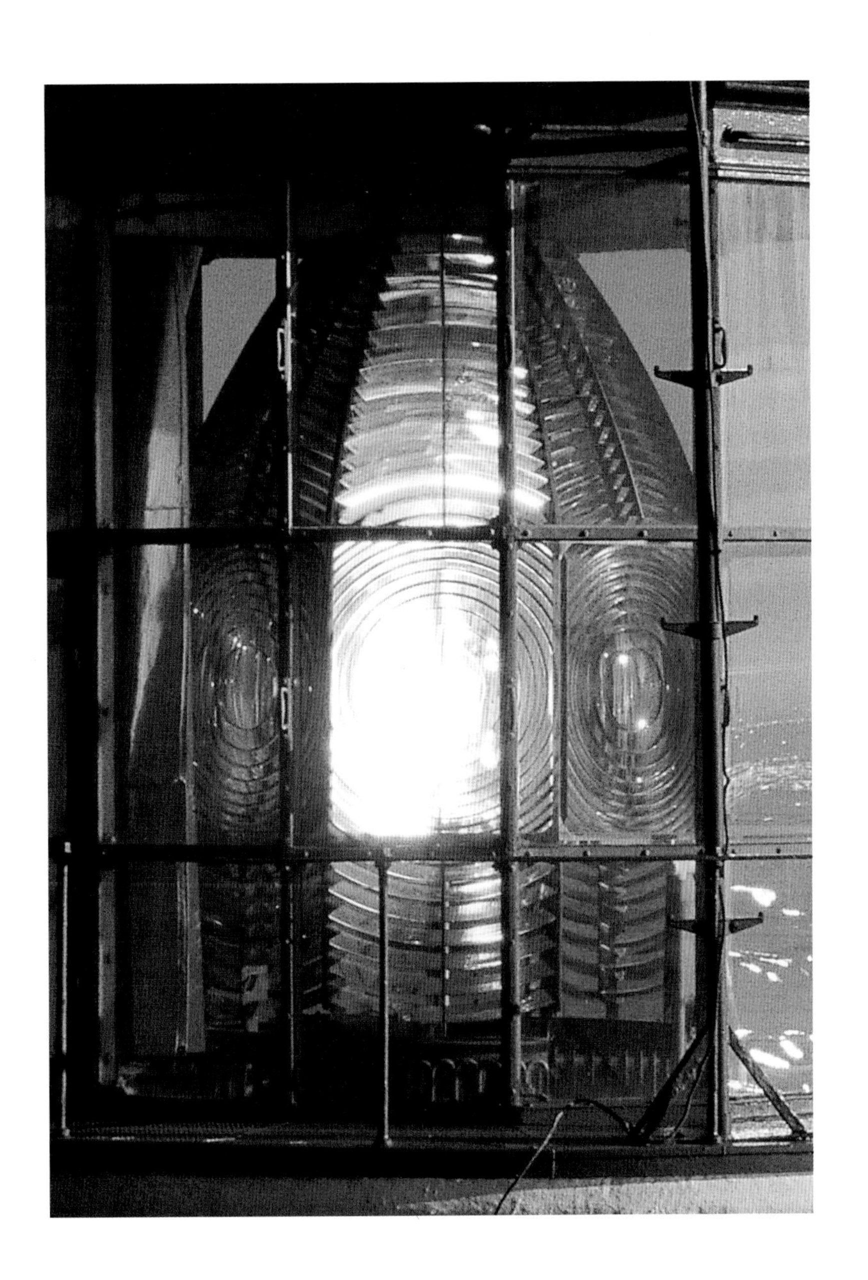

ANATOMY OF THE LIGHTHOUSE

Michael J. Rhein

Saraband

Above: *A lighthouse built on the highest available ground at Hiddensee, Germany.*

Page 1: *The first-order Fresnel lens at Oregon's Heceta Head Lighthouse.*

Page 2: *Cape Lookout Light, North Carolina.*

Page 3: *Lens detail, St. John's Point Light, County Down, Northern Ireland.*

FOR PETER AND CLAIRE MALAN

"I can think of no other edifice constructed by man as altruistic as a lighthouse. They were built only to serve. They weren't built for any other purpose..."

—George Bernard Shaw

Published by Saraband (Scotland) Limited, The Arthouse, 752-756 Argyle Street, Glasgow G3 8UJ, Scotland

ISBN: 1-887354-27-1
Printed in China

10 9 8 7 6 5 4 3 2 1

FOREWORD

This book fills an important gap in the literature about lighthouses by exploring the many facets of a basic question. Addressing what should be the premise of any discussion on this topic (often barely touched upon in other books of this genre), it answers the crucial question: "What is a lighthouse?"

This question is both simple and complex, involving as it does such factors as siting, design, construction materials, illumination and the various hazards presented by given locations around the world. *Anatomy of a Lighthouse* takes an in-depth look at all of these factors and more. They are explained and illustrated to capture not only the beauty of these diverse aids to navigation, but the skill and tenacity involved in their construction and safekeeping.

One message that I hope comes through in this book is the need to preserve these important maritime treasures for future generations. Lighthouses are not simply scenic attractions, dotting our coastlines like so many exclamation marks. They represent the incredibly difficult and far-sighted achievements of our forefathers.

In the United States, lighthouse construction was the subject of our first Public Works Act, signed by George Washington in 1789. It is considered "the first great work of the American people." The enormous effort and ingenuity displayed by our ancestors in building these impressive structures forms a chronicle of epic proportions, and the ever-vigilant lives of their heroic keepers is legendary. These inspiring stories must not be lost. They are important reminders in our fast-paced and increasingly impersonal modern culture that we are, indeed, "our brothers' keepers."

I recommend this book to the reader, trusting that it will stand as a tribute to these wonderful buildings we call lighthouses, and that, in turning its pages, you will gain a better understanding and appreciation for the evolutionary process of making worldwide maritime travel and commerce ever safer and more secure.

—James Hyland, Founder and President,
The Lighthouse Preservation Society

CONTENTS

NANTUCKET

INTRODUCTION
A History of Lighthouse Evolution

***Previous pages**: Brightly painted light towers like this one in Germany's Schleswig-Holstein are intended to be both distinctive and clearly visible from a distance during daylight hours in clear conditions, when their lights are extinguished.*

Indeed they were very close to the Lighthouse now. There it loomed up, stark and straight, glaring white and black, and one could see the waves breaking in white splinters like smashed glass against the rocks.

—Virginia Woolf
To the Lighthouse (1927)

It is a measure of the success of our lighthouses that we take them for granted. As wide-eyed children many of us may have listened enthralled to stories of the heroism of lighthouse keepers, yet when we think of lighthouses it may be only when we are safely home on a stormy night, listening to the wind howling and the rain lashing against the windows, sparing a thought for the sea-buffeted ships being guided to land and safety by the steady beam of a lighthouse. In our age of cost-cutting and unprecedented technical innovation, however, the majority of the world's surviving lighthouses have been deemed both impractical and overly expensive aids to navigation. Having faithfully fulfilled their life-saving function over the centuries, and stoically endured all that the sea has thrown at them, they are being replaced by cheaper aids to navigation, like buoys and aerobeacons. And even where they have been spared, their keepers' roles have usually been made obsolete by automation. Thus, they have become unoccupied, their lonely vigilance punctuated only by occasional inspection visits.

Although its traditional components may have been superseded by technology, the lighthouse is an archetypal symbol that represents a significant triumph in humanity's continuing battle against the vagaries of the temperamental sea. Romantic as the light tower may appear, rising as it does in solitary magnificence above the untamable sea, its light has a more profound significance. For on a symbolic, as well as a practical level, the light that it projects is a beacon of hope. And from prehistoric times, when humanity first began to express cosmic concepts through mythology and religious metaphors, to the present day, humans have equated light with the hope, goodness and order that illuminate and vanquish the evil, chaos and destructive powers of the forces of darkness.

This is just one of the profound reasons why lighthouses exert such a powerful hold on our imagination, and why sea dogs and landlubbers alike are rebelling against the state of dilapidation into which many historic beacons have fallen. Just when their existence is most threatened, individuals and societies around the world are becoming aware of the need to preserve the heritage of heroism and hope that lighthouses embody and are uniting in the battle to do so. Yet despite our strong affinity with them, lighthouses as we know them—solid structures that were built for the sole purpose of alerting sailors to maritime dangers and guiding them to the safety of the shore—are only a few centuries old. So how, and why, did the lighthouse evolve? What is the story that underpins the remarkable achievement of the lighthouse builders?

FROM BONFIRE BEACONS TO THE PHAROS OF ALEXANDRIA

Every sailor has a healthy respect for the sea: calm waters may suddenly become turbulent; gentle breezes may be whipped up into gale-force winds; and hapless mariners may suddenly find themselves in life-or-death situations. Even today, when vessels are equipped with such high-tech equipment as radar and satellite-navigation systems, and are guided by reliable aids to navigation in most international waters, the changeability of the sea can never be underestimated. Without these modern advantages, what hazards must the seafarers of earliest times have faced, and how did they attempt to overcome them?

Humanity has always had an uneasy relationship with the sea. Since the time that our earliest ancestors first learned to build boats, people have plundered the sea for fish and have crossed it for the purposes of trade and warfare. In so doing, however, they risked their lives, for not only is the sea dangerously unpredictable, but the world's coastlines are strewn with such deathtraps as submerged reefs and treacherous currents that may undo the most skillful navigator. Beacons, and later lighthouses, therefore served two essential purposes: first, to guide mariners directly to landfall, and, second, to warn them away from navigational hazards.

At night, especially when the Moon was obscured by cloud or fog—a quality of darkness that is almost impossible for many of us to visualize in our age of nearly ubiquitous electric lighting and light pollution—the ancient coastline would have appeared indistinguishable from the sea. The people of prehistoric times and beyond used the only means available to them to guide their seafaring folk home safely. Thus, the first beacons were simple bonfires, kindled either on the beach or on hill- or clifftops above the shore to provide a focal point for the community's fishermen returning to land after dark. Inevitably, no archeological evidence survives for such beacons, although some of the earliest literary references to them are contained in the *Iliad* and the *Odyssey*, the epic works of the eighth-century BC poet Homer.

Although it, too, no longer survives, historians agree that the first "dedicated" lighthouse was the Pharos of Alexandria, which was classed as one of antiquity's Seven Wonders of the World. Another of these wondrous structures believed to have played a navigational role was the Colossus of Rhodes, a bronze statue of Helios, the Greek god of the Sun, which rose 100 feet (30 meters) above the harbor of the island of Rhodes. Before its destruction by an earthquake in about 224 BC, it was said to guide vessels into the harbor by means of fires lit inside and visible through its eyes and a hand.

Left: Built during the third century BC, the Pharos of Alexandria was one of the Seven Wonders of the Ancient World.

Built to guide trading vessels to Alexandria, Egypt—then the world's most important port—the Pharos was completed about 280 BC, during the reign of Ptolemy II, Egypt's Macedonian ruler, on the Mediterranean island of Pharos, off northern Egypt. The reason for the Pharos's construction was that the Nile Delta offered no discernible features on which sailors could orient themselves. Given the flatness of the surrounding landscape, with its reputed height of 436 feet (133 meters), as well as a light that could be seen 40 miles (65 kilometers) out to sea, it is perhaps no wonder that this unique tower should have been regarded as miraculous by contemporary commentators.

The lighthouse that the Pharos's architect, Sostratus of Cnidus, designed was as elaborate as it was functional. Having constructed a base about 360 feet (110 meters) square, Sostratus then erected three levels: first, a square tier 236 feet (72 meters) tall and 100 feet (30 meters) square; second, an octagonal story 115 feet (35 meters) high; and, finally, a cylindrical tier 85 feet (26 meters) tall, on which was perched the brazier in which the fire burned. The light-keepers gained access to the brazier by means of a spiral ramp. During the thirteenth century, the Islamic geographer Edrisi commented on the Pharos's "excellence of construction and strength," noting admiringly: "Not only is it constructed of a fine-quality stone...but the various blocks are so strongly cemented together with melted lead that the whole is imperishable." Edrisi was wrong, however: having incurred some damage in AD 641, when Alexandria fell to Islamic troops, the Pharos was ultimately destroyed by an earthquake in 1346. The rubble from its ruins was incorporated into an Islamic fortress in 1477. Yet the legend of the Pharos endures to this day, not least in the linguistic tribute paid to it by the French and Spanish languages, whose words for "lighthouse" are respectively *phare* and *faro*.

***Below:** The breakwater lighthouse that guides ships into southeastern England's principal port, Dover, stands beneath the famous White Cliffs. Beyond, between the profiles of the Norman Dover Castle (center left) and the Saxon St. Mary-in-Castro Church (center right), the ruined tower of the first-century Roman* pharos *can be discerned.*

ROMAN LIGHTHOUSES

The Roman Empire relied on the Pharos to guide its vessels safely into the port of Alexandria, where they could obtain abundant supplies of grain with which to feed Roman citizens. Gradually, the Romans, too, erected lighthouses of their own at various strategic maritime trading posts in their vast and sprawling empire, such as the Portus, built during the reign of Emperor Trajan on the mouth of the River Tiber to assist ships carrying grain from Alexandria to reach Rome safely. By AD 400 it is estimated that there were about thirty Roman lighthouses.

Although many renowned Roman lighthouses, such as that at Rome's primary port of Ostia (built in about AD 50), no longer survive, the few that remain attest to their prevalent style—relatively short and sturdy towers at the top of which a fire burned. The ruins of the lighthouse at Dover, England, for example, which was built during the first century AD, indicate an octagonal stone tower 29 feet (24 meters) tall. Across the English Channel, the deranged Emperor Caligula, who firmly believed that he had challenged and subdued the sea god, Neptune, ordered in around AD 40 that a lighthouse be constructed at Boulogne, France, to commemorate his resounding "victory." With the decline of the Roman Empire, the resultant octagonal, brick-and-stone structure, which was 124 feet (40 meters) high, fell into disuse, although it was reputedly restored during the reign of the Holy Roman emperor, Charlemagne, beginning in AD 800. The "Old Man of Bullen," as the English called it, or the *Tour d'Ordre*, as it was known to the French, finally succumbed to the sea in 1644, fatally weakened by erosion and the plundering of its stone.

Despite the demise of most of the lighthouses of classical times, it is a Roman lighthouse that has the distinction of being the oldest tower still serving the same function as it did when it was built, during the second century AD. The lighthouse that stands on a hill north of La Coruña, at the mouth of the River Guadalquivir on Spain's Galician coast, is steeped in mythology. To the Romans, it was the Tower of Hercules, in whose foundations the Greek hero was said to have buried the corpse of his defeated foe, the Giant of Grion, while in Celtic lore it was sacred to the sea goddess Brigantia. A rock at the base of the lighthouse, however, confirms its Roman origins with the inscription "Dedicated to Marte Augustus, Cayo Servio Lupo [Gaius Servius Lupus], architect of Aeminium, in accordance with his oath," and the square stone tower, which was about 100 feet (30 meters) tall, was mentioned by many Roman writers. Like the lighthouse at Boulogne, however, that at La Coruña mirrored the decline of the empire of its builders, and by the sixteenth century, hundreds of years of neglect, warfare and plunder had reduced it to a shell. Although the increased importance of trade to Spain prompted its refurbishment in 1682, the lighthouse soon fell into disrepair again, and it was not until the late eighteenth century that concerted efforts were made to repair and relight it. Supervised by Galicia's marine lieutenant, Eustaquio Giannini, workmen covered the tower with granite cladding to strengthen its structure and built an interior stairway to give access to the stone lantern that they erected at the apex. In 1791 La Coruña's light shone out to sea once more. Initially lit by a coal fire, which was then replaced with oil lights, in 1847 a Fresnel lens fueled by olive oil was placed in the lantern. Thereafter, the modernization of La Coruña kept pace with technical developments, a mechanical lamp that used paraffin being installed in 1883, followed by an incandescent petroleum-vapor lamp in 1904, and finally by electrification in 1921.

MEDIEVAL LIGHTHOUSES

By AD 500 the Roman Empire had ceased to exist in the West, and Europe entered an era that historians call the Dark Ages, a term that applies as much to the lighting of its coastlines as to its society. Although little, if any, lighthouse construction was undertaken during this period, some attempts were made to assist mariners—monks, for example, lighting fires on the towers of their churches. In the Far East, too, sacred structures were often pressed into lighthouse service at this time.

By around AD 1100 commerce between European peoples had started to burgeon, and this increase in trading activity, in turn, stimulated renewed interest in lighthouse construction. The countries that led the way in lighting their shores were those that relied on maritime trade for their influence and prosperity, especially Italy and France, as well as Germany, Scandinavia and Britain. The majority of Europe's significant medieval lighthouses were built of stone and lit by fires variously fueled by wood, coal, or oil.

Along with those at Messina, Tino and Venice, the most notable Italian lighthouses of the Middle Ages include those at Meloria, Livorno (Leghorn) and Genoa. Following its construction on a treacherous shoal in 1157, Meloria's lighthouse was damaged as a result of the internecine warfare waged by Italy's city states and was completely destroyed in 1290. Its replacement was erected on a rock in Livorno Harbor in 1304. This was not the first lighthouse at Livorno, however: the first had been built in 1154, with funding from the Republic of Pisa, which, after the tower's destruction at the hands of Genoan forces in 1284, also paid for its replacement. The lighthouse that stands at Livorno today was built in 1956, using the original stone from the structure that was demolished by enemy action during World War II. The Lanterna of Genoa, which was first established as an aid to navigation in

Neuwerk

The Story of Germany's Oldest Lighthouse

Although Hamburg is Germany's largest port, it is something of a geographical curiosity in that it is more than 160 miles (100 kilometers) from the North Sea, or, more precisely, from the mouth of the River Elbe. The need initially to gain, and then to maintain, free access to the North Sea dominates Hamburg's history and also explains why Germany's oldest lighthouse was built on the island of Neuwerk in the estuary of the Elbe.

Having been established as the fortress *Hammaburg* during the ninth century, Hamburg grew into a leading northern European trading center, its position strengthened by the establishment and growth of the Hanseatic League during the fourteenth and fifteenth centuries. Navigating the River Elbe between the North Sea and Hamburg's harbor presented early trading ships with three specific problems. First, the local coastal region consists solely of mudflats and shoals. Second, the region's tidal action causes extreme differences in the depth of the water. And, third, at that time vessels faced the threat of attacks at sea by privateers and pirates from Frisia and Dithmarsch, as well as ambushes by land-based robber barons, a dual peril that worsened about 1270.

Such maritime hazards finally forced the citizens of Hamburg to take action: in 1286 they sought the permission of the region's ruler, the duke of Saxony, to erect a beacon on a small uninhabited island 5.6 miles (9 kilometers) from the coast. The island's Friesian name was *Nige Oog* (the Low German for "New Island"). The small wooden tower that resulted housed a beacon consisting of an open fire burning in a copper pan. Shortly after its completion, however, Hamburg's town council decided to replace the structure with a fortified stone tower in order to protect it against attacks by pirates and robber barons.

Work on the replacement tower was started in 1299 and was finished eleven years later. The building materials had to be transported by ship from the mainland to the island—a trip that was possible only at high tide—making construction of the tower a slow and laborious task. Erratic blocks (boulders that had been transported to and deposited at the site by glaciers during the Ice Age) were used for the tower's massive foundations. Bricks, placed in what is known as a "cloister" pattern, finished the upper part to create walls that were 5 to 8 feet (1.5 to 2.5 meters) thick. When the building was finally completed, the solid square tower rose 125 feet (38 meters) above the sea. Accommodation was provided for city senators on the third floor, while a large storeroom below was set aside to protect marine wreckage from attempted theft. A Hamburg councilor, along with ten armed men, took up occupation of the tower over Easter in 1310. It was this new structure, *Nige Wark* (from the Low German, meaning "New Work") that gave the island the name by which it is known today: Neuwerk.

Apart from a brief interruption between 1937 and 1962, Neuwerk has belonged to Hamburg since 1394, when the city forcibly appropriated it, along with other territory around the Elbe Estuary. The tower at Neuwerk remained primarily a defensive structure until the nineteenth century, its beacon being maintained constantly only from 1761. It was not until 1814 that the advent of the steam ship caused the tower to be fitted out to contemporary lighthouse standards. Before then no ship would sail up the Elbe to Hamburg at night.

Today, Neuwerk continues to perform a commercially and navigationally important—indeed, indispensable—function at the mouth of the Elbe. Its light, which shines at a height of 127 feet (38.7 meters), was first displayed in 1892. The 700 millimeter drum lens, housed in a copper casing, flashes a white, red and green signal that can be seen up to 16 nautical miles (29.6 kilometers) away.

Neuwerk has the distinction of being the oldest functioning German lighthouse, as well as the oldest preserved building in the Free and Hanseatic Town of Hamburg, to give the city its full title. Times have changed since it was first constructed, however: the island on which it stands is now inhabited, and the mudflats that surround it have become a nature reserve, while the formerly isolated light tower itself has become a popular tourist attraction.

—Heinz Lindenberg,
Local historian, Hamburg, Germany

1161, received a tower in 1321; in a curiosity of history, records show that Christopher Columbus's uncle, Antonio Columbus (or Columbo), was employed as its keeper in 1449. When it, too, was damaged by fighting, it was reconstructed under the supervision of Martino de Rosio in 1544. The Lanterna's sixteenth-century incarnation (which survives today) consisted of a square foundation supporting two square stone tiers, stacked one above the other, each 100 feet (30 meters) in height, on top of which stood a cylindrical lantern. To avert the lightning that this 200-foot (61-meter) structure attracted with regularity, a statue of St. Christopher, the patron saint of travelers, was placed nearby.

France's most famous medieval lighthouse was built to replace one that had been erected during the ninth century on the island of Cordouan, which lies in the estuary of the Gironde River east of Bordeaux, a leading center of the French wine trade. The purpose of this lighthouse and its successors was to warn mariners away from the lethal rocks that made reaching port such a dangerous exercise, and like many early European navigational aids, it was maintained by monks. During his governorship of the province of Guyenne, Edward the Black Prince, the warrior son of the English king Edward III, ordered the overhaul of the centuries-old, wave-swept lighthouse. In accordance with his wishes, a wooden tower was first raised on the island in 1355. It was replaced in 1360 with a polygonal stone tower rising 53 feet (16 meters) above the sea, alongside which accommodations and a chapel were built for the attendant monks. By the sixteenth century, however, the tower had become irreparably dilapidated, and King Henri III of France charged architect Louis de Foix with its reconstruction. Work began in 1584, but due to problems of subsidence that resulted in the island's becoming totally submerged, it was not completed until 1611. During the twenty-seven years that it took to construct the lighthouse at Cordouan, the baton of command was passed from de Foix to his son, and from him to François Beuscher, the project's chief mason.

Left: The elaborate sixteenth-century lighthouse at Cordouan, France, built against almost impossible odds to a design by Louis de Foix.

The marvel of engineering that finally shone its wood-fueled light over the Gironde stood on a circular foundation 135 feet (41 meters) in diameter, protected by a wall 28 feet (8.5 meters) tall. Constructed of ashlar (cut stone), its interior included a chapel that was as ornately decorated as the exterior, including statues and all manner of elaborate architectural ornamentation. Joseph Teulère modified the structure between 1788 and 1791, adding height to the tower by replacing its upper section with a circular stone tower 60 feet (18 meters) tall, and also providing the lighthouse keepers with improved, basement-level accommodation and storage facilities.

EDDYSTONE AND THE DAWN OF THE MODERN ERA

Although not all of the medieval lighthouses have survived, a study of contemporaneous navigational charts made by D. Alan Stevenson (a scion of the famous Stevenson dynasty of lighthouse engineers, responsible for building eighty-one beacons) suggests that thirty-four lighthouses lit Europe's shores, rivers and harbors by 1600, a figure that had swelled to 175 in 1800. The reason for this dramatic increase in the number of European lighthouses was the rapid advances that were made in the fields of science and technology during the late eighteenth century, as well as the nineteenth—in short, the Industrial Revolution. If any one lighthouse can be said to embody the transition from the medieval to the modern era, it is Eddystone, or, more precisely, the third Eddystone lighthouse of 1759.

Eddystone Rocks, in the English Channel, lie 14 miles (22.5 kilometers) off the important port of Plymouth, in southwestern England. An entry made in his log by the captain of the Pilgrim ship *The Mayflower* on September 6, 1620, spoke for many when he recorded his relief at having successfully negotiated this "wicked reef...[that] must always be dreaded by mariners." It was not until the end of the seventeenth century, however, that Britain's first offshore lighthouse was erected on this hazardous site by an eccentric dilettante ship owner, two of whose ships the reef had claimed. It took Henry Winstanley from 1696 until 1698 to complete his 80-foot (24-meter) wooden, brick and iron tower, which was supported by a foundation 14 feet (4 meters) in diameter anchored by twelve stanchions drilled into the reef. In 1699 Winstanley found it necessary to reinforce the structure with stone and iron and to increase its height to 120 feet (36.5 meters). His efforts were in vain, however, for in 1703 the lighthouse—and Winstanley with it—was swept away by waves during a terrible storm. The second lighthouse at Eddystone was erected by John Rudyerd, a silk merchant, in 1709. Bolted to the reef, the conical stone-and-timber tower was clad with oak, a flammable material that caused its destruction when the wooden lantern room caught fire in 1755.

Work on the third Eddystone lighthouse began in 1756, under the supervision of John Smeaton (who, unlike his predecessors, was an engineer), and was finished in 1759. Recognizing the importance of providing stability with a solid, supportive foundation, Smeaton's solution was to taper the tower inward and upward from its wide, circular base, comparing his concept to an oak tree, which is "broad at its base, curves inwards at its waist, becomes narrower towards the top"; "We seldom hear of a mature oak being uprooted," he added. The curved tower itself consisted of interlocked, dovetailed blocks of Portland stone, rather than wood, an innovation that would be adopted by future lighthouse builders. Smeaton's lighthouse, which was lit by twenty-four tallow candles, withstood all that the sea could throw at it until 1882, when, due to the undermining of its foundation by a cave, the upper section of the lighthouse was removed and shipped to Plymouth (where it was reassembled as a monument). Although the lower section was left in situ, Eddystone's replacement lighthouse was erected on a neighboring site by James Douglass. Built of granite, Douglass's tower survives to this day, rising 49 meters (161 feet) above the sea.

Smeaton's successful design led other builders to use Eddystone's plans as a starting point before making modifications of their own to meet the demands of individual sites. Among the most notable of Smeaton's successors was Robert Stevenson (grandfather of the novelist Robert Louis Stevenson), who between 1807 and 1811 planned and oversaw the construction of the Bell Rock, or Inchcape, lighthouse, 12 miles (19 kilometers) off Arbroath, on Scotland's eastern coast. Like Eddystone Rocks, Bell Rock had both a murderous history and a submerged reef—indeed, in 1799, eight years before work on the lighthouse began, at least seventy vessels were wrecked on it. Accommodated on a lightship, and working in the most difficult conditions, Stevenson's workmen dug a hole in the rock 42 feet (13 meters) in diameter before bolting the first of a series of successive courses of dovetailed granite to the foundation. When it was completed, the lighthouse stood 118 feet (36 meters) tall and displayed an Argand lamp, surrounded by rotating parabolic reflectors that, with the aid of both red and white glass, flashed a distinctive two-color light. It represented a triumph of will over adversity.

The Stevensons were responsible for such other lighthouses of note, to name but a few, as Robert Stevenson's Isle of May Lighthouse (1816), at the entrance to the Firth of Forth, which resembles a baronial folly, and his son, Alan Stevenson's, Skerryvore Lighthouse (1844), off the Isle of Tyree, which was fitted with a revolving dioptric Fresnel lens. It was largely due to the efforts of this remarkable family of engineers that Scotland's coastline became one of the best lit in the world.

Nor did the Stevensons confine their focus to Scotland's shores. Following Commodore Matthew Perry's mission to Japan, and the consequent opening up of this traditionally isolationist country to foreign trade in 1854, international pressure was put on Japan to erect a series of lighthouses along its shores. Although Japan had previously provided local mariners with aids to navigation, in common with many other countries, these had taken the form of basic beacons of fire; Japanese authorities conceded that if their island nation was to benefit from international trade, its lights should be in keeping with the industrial age. Thus it was that David and Thomas Stevenson, Robert's younger sons, traveled to Japan (among other countries, including India) to design and construct its first modern lighthouse, which was soon followed by others.

The increase in international trade, as well as advances in lighthouse technology, resulted in a significant number of beacons springing up along the world's shorelines. The Macquarie Lighthouse in Sydney, Australia, which was completed by convicts as laborers in 1817, is one of Oceania's oldest, while a series of lighthouses was also built during the second half of the nineteenth century in New Zealand, from cast-iron plates imported from England. The first, in 1859, was the Pencarrow Head Lighthouse on the Pacific Ocean. On the African continent, South Africa led the way with its Green Point Lighthouse on the Cape of Good Hope, erected in 1824. The maritime nations of Europe also added to their lighthouse stock. Germany, for exam-

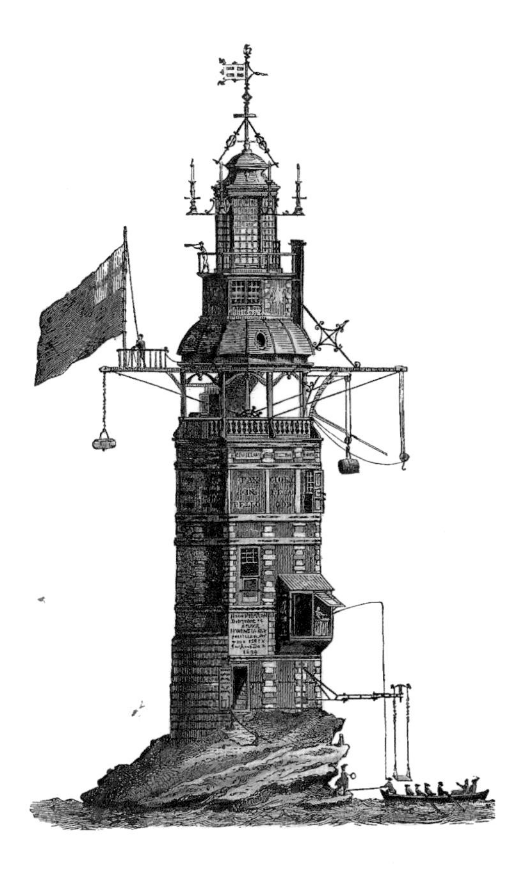

***Left**: Henry Winstanley's lighthouse at Eddystone, off Plymouth, England, was a remarkable achievement despite its relatively short existence.*

ple, in 1854, constructed the first of twelve light towers that today provide illumination for Bremerhaven's Weser River. Other northern European nations both built and improved, often replacing existing lever lights with light towers, as on Denmark's Baagoe Island, in the Sound of Little Belt, which received a brick lighthouse in 1816, and at Kvitsøy, on the North Sea in Norway, where a stone tower was constructed in 1829. The historical significance of such innovative structures as the Green Point Light is seen by the fact that many lighthouse administrations now use them as their headquarters.

LIGHTHOUSE ADMINISTRATION

Like most countries with coastlines, and a concomitant need for lighthouses, the story of their evolution is as closely linked to the vicissitudes of their administration as it is to economic or technological progress. The oldest such administrative organization is England and Wales's Corporation of Trinity House, which evolved from a guild of river pilots based in Deptford Strond, on the River Thames, that requested, and received, a royal charter in 1514. The Brethren of Trinity House first assumed responsibility for caring for retired pilots, or their widows and orphans, but the Seamarks Act of 1566 granted them the right to erect seamarks, and then, in 1594, beacons and buoys. During the seventeenth century, the Crown bestowed its right to award lighthouse-building patents upon Trinity House, whereupon the members considered the merits of each application and bestowed patents accordingly. Many lighthouses remained privately operated, however, their owners charging light dues from the vessels that benefited from their beacons. Such a system was clearly open to abuse, and in 1836 an act of parliament remedied this situation by stipulating that all of the lighthouses in private hands should be transferred to Trinity House, a procedure that was completed in 1841. Changes were made to the administration of lighthouses in Scotland and Ireland, too. Responsibility for Scottish and Manx (Isle of Man) lighthouses was given to the Commissioners of Northern Lighthouses, or the Northern Lighthouse Board, in 1786, and the Commissioners for Irish Lights assumed a similar function for Ireland in 1867. Today the three bodies receive their revenues from the General Lighthouse Fund, which is, in turn, funded by user charges.

Other early nationalized lighthouse services include those of Scandinavia (Denmark's was established in 1650), although most maritime countries did not follow suit until the nineteenth century. The geographical extent and complexity of the United States, however, as well as its importance in terms of world trade, meant that from the young republic's earliest days, an efficient and well-coordinated lighthouse administration would be required to supervise erection and maintenance. Ultimately, some 1,500 lighthouses would guide mariners through U.S. waters over a period of almost four centuries.

LIGHTING THE NEW WORLD

The first purpose-built lighthouse on the mainland of the Americas is believed to have been the Santo Antonio Lighthouse (1698), which watches over the harbor of Salvador City in Brazil. It was not until 1716 that North America raised its first beacon: Boston Harbor Light, on Little Brewster Island, in Boston Harbor, Massachusetts. Constructed under British colonial administration, it was a cylindrical stone tower, standing some 60 to 75 feet (18 to 23 meters) above sea level. It served until 1776, when it was targeted by a British naval bombardment early in the American War of Independence. (Rebuilt in 1783 and heightened in 1859, the replacement conical masonry tower measures 89 feet (27 meters) and remains the oldest operational lighthouse in the United States.) Canada's first lighthouse (and North America's second) was the tower built at Fort Louisbourg, on Cape Breton Island, in 1734. Having survived a lantern fire in 1736, in 1758 this French-Canadian structure, which was 70 feet (21.3 meters) tall, was then devastated by the cannon fire of the British Navy, its replacement not built until 1842. Today, therefore, it is the Sambro Island Lighthouse (1759), in Nova Scotia, that has the distinction of being Canada's oldest functioning light.

Boston Light was one of twelve that were erected along North America's East Coast prior to the American Revolution. Although the design of each varied to suit its location, and the materials used were locally sourced, all were either timber or stone towers and none exceeded 90 feet (27 meters) in height. The only one to survive relatively intact that still functions as a lighthouse is that at Sandy Hook, New Jersey, which was constructed in 1764.

Following the establishment of the United States in 1789, the new federal government moved swiftly to centralize administration of the aids to navigation that it had inherited from Britain—indeed, in only the ninth official act of Congress, the new Treasury Department was designated responsible for their construction and upkeep. Another measure of their importance is the fact that President George Washington initially played an active role in lighthouse administration, although the demands on his time eventually resulted in the delegation of this work to the Secretary of the Treasury, Alexander Hamilton. Following the committed leadership of Albert Gallatin, Secretary of the Treasury from 1801 to 1814, the baton was passed to the Commissioner of Revenue, until this office was abolished in 1820 and Congress transferred the responsibility for lighthouse administration to the Fifth Auditor of the Treasury.

Most of the lighthouses that were built under the respective regimes of the Secretary of the Treasury, the Commissioner of Revenue, and the Fifth Auditor of the Treasury were so unimpressively constructed that they have since had to be replaced. This was in part because modern construction techniques were still in their infancy. Financial considerations also played a significant role in rendering the lighthouses of this era unsatisfactory: contracts for new construction were typically awarded to the cheapest, not the best, proposal, while the on-site regulation of lighthouses was undertaken by collectors of customs, who retained 2.5 percent of the revenue they garnered. It was unfortunate that a period of booming trade coincided with the tenure of office of Stephen Pleasonton, Fifth Auditor of the Treasury from 1820 to 1852 and a proudly parsimonious man. Despite the invention of the Fresnel lens in 1822, for example, Pleasonton insisted on lighting U.S. shores with Winslow Lewis's inferior, but less expensive, lamp-and-

***Below:** Construction of the lighthouse at scenic Portland Head, Maine, was begun in 1787. When it went into service in 1791, it became the first light tower completed under the auspices of the U.S. government.*

reflector system. It must have been a source of both frustration and pride to Pleasonton that during his regime, the number of U.S. lights increased from fifty-five in 1820 to 331 (plus forty-two lightships) in 1852. Most lighthouses of this era were onshore structures, either soaring masonry or brick towers, or one-and-a-half-story buildings from which a relatively short integral tower protruded.

Unsurprisingly, in 1837 the mounting deluge of complaints from mariners prompted Congress to appoint a board of navy commissioners to undertake a detailed survey of the state of the nation's lights. Taking many of their recommendations into account, Congress created ten lighthouse districts in 1838 and dispatched a naval officer to investigate the lights in each. Although the resultant reports were scathing, little was done to remedy the situation until 1851, when Congress commissioned a second specialist committee to undertake another nationwide survey. The committee reached a similarly dismal conclusion, urging immediate action and making detailed recommendations for improvements. Congress's response was immediate, and in 1852 it created the Lighthouse Board, which consisted of nine unpaid, but expert, members, and twelve lighthouse districts, to each of which a naval officer was assigned to assume responsibility for the erection and maintenance of its lighthouses. In time, the Lighthouse Board also took over the functions that had previously been delegated to the local collectors of customs.

This careful reorganization and much-needed injection of expertise had remarkably swift and effective results. By 1861 most U.S. lighthouses had been equipped with Fresnel lenses, while an intensive program of building offshore screwpile, dovetailed-stone and caisson lighthouses—to name a few of the types that are explored in detail later—was well underway. Indeed, by 1910, when the Bureau of Lighthouses, or the Lighthouse Service, was established, 11,713 navigational aids existed (of which 1,200 were lighthouses), both within U.S. waterways and along the coasts. The reason for Congress's decision to transfer the responsibility for aids to navigation from the Lighthouse Board to the Lighthouse Service was by no means a reflection on the Lighthouse Board's performance, but was instead the result of the perceived need to civilianize the administration of lighthouses. Under the Lighthouse Service's commissioner, George R. Putnam, who served as such until 1935, the nation's beacons were gradually electrified, and radio beacons were introduced after 1921.

A logical step was taken in 1939, when the task of administering the nation's lighthouses was transferred to the U.S. Coast Guard. Active lighthouses have been maintained by the Coast Guard's Aids to Navigation Teams (ANTs) since 1980.

RUNNING THE LIGHTHOUSE

Many people regret the disappearance of the traditional keepers—the human face of the lighthouse—who had to endure conditions of punishingly relentless labor in hazardous, fire-prone and polluted structures, and who experienced stultifying boredom and loneliness punctuated by incidences of drama and danger that all too often cost them their lives. Indeed, although many administrative organizations around the world gave careful consideration to the practicalities of running their lighthouses, it fell to the keepers to transform the blueprint into reality.

In order to enable the keepers to do their jobs efficiently, and to make them as comfortable as possible, the anatomy of the lighthouse included far more components than simply the tower and lantern with which most people are familiar. The keeper's personal quarters were located either within a building that was separate from, but adjacent to, the light tower or, if the tower was integral, within the structure that supported it. Calls of nature were answered in privies that were originally located outside the lighthouse (unless the lighthouse was offshore, in which case they were cantilevered to extend from the gallery below the lantern). Later, these facilities were incorporated into the structure. Since many lighthouses were surrounded by saltwater, a source of potable water had to be provided for the keeper's personal and professional needs. In some areas, rainwater was channeled into tanks from guttering on the roof of the tower, while in drier regions, catch basins and cisterns were used to collect and store as much rainwater as possible.

From his or her quarters, the keeper could reach the watch-tower below the lantern by climbing the stairs that spiraled around the interior walls of the tower (landings were placed at regular intervals to provide rest-stops and additional storage). During the nineteenth century, the oil that fueled the light was stored either within the basement of the lighthouse itself, or in a specially constructed outbuilding nearby. When the more flammable kerosene became the preferred fuel, however, it was necessary to build a separate fireproof oil house for reasons of safety. Today's automated lighthouses often require outbuildings, too, in which to house the generator. In addition to tending the light, keepers often had to operate the fog signal, which could be housed either in a stand-alone tower situated below the lantern, or in a separate structure close to the lighthouse. Other light-station components might include a vegetable garden, a barn in which livestock was kept, a storehouse, workroom and boathouse.

A LIVING HERITAGE

Despite the historical importance of the keepers' role, today they are an almost obsolete breed. The rapid development of such modern aids to navigation as aerobeacons and large navigational buoys (LNBs), along with electronic on-vessel innovations including radar, sonar and satellite-navigation systems, have obviated the need for most manned stations. Not only are these technologies more reliable than the traditional lighthouse-and-keeper partnership, but, perhaps more pertinently, they are also safer, easier to maintain and cheaper. Nevertheless, many lighthouses retain their navigational role, whether as unlit daymarks or as automated beacons.

Over the past few centuries, those who have been entrusted with the care of the world's aids to navigation have benefited immeasurably from increased international cooperation and shared information, particularly since the establishment of the International Association of Lighthouses (I.A.L.A.), based in Paris, France, in 1957, to which about eighty countries belong. As well as introducing measures that have been uniformly adopted by its members, such as the I.A.L.A. International Maritime Buoyage System of 1982, the I.A.L.A. continues to work toward improving the safety of the world's seas and waterways. In addition, many national and local societies have sprung up over recent years with the aim of ensuring that our lighthouse heritage is preserved. When a lighthouse is no longer viable, for example, they often rescue it from dereliction to serve as a museum.

This book shares the aim of those who seek to commemorate and celebrate the vital role that lighthouses and other aids to navigation have played in human history. By describing and assessing the apparently insurmountable challenges involved in the construction, operation and maintenance of individual lighthouses—challenges that were overcome by a combination of ingenuity, bravery and dogged determination—it will inspire a renewed respect for the pioneers who first envisaged, and then realized in increasingly sophisticated forms, the anatomy of the lighthouse.

NATURE'S POWER

Weather, Oceans & Coastal Geology

Previous pages: *During winter months, lighthouses sited in ice-prone locations must be resistant to the incursion of water, which expands when it freezes, causing potentially destructive fissures in the fabric or joints of the structure. For wave-swept sites, like this light station in Charlevoix, Michigan, which was built on a pier, the challenges to engineers are even more exacting, because the foundations must be able to withstand the tremendous force generated by moving ice sheets.*

Opposite: *The famous lighthouse at Cape Hatteras, North Carolina, lies on a barrier island in the Atlantic Ocean that is subject to storms sometimes severe enough to change the contours of the island itself. Prolonged erosion forced engineers to move this masonry tower—the tallest lighthouse in the United States—to a new location farther inland in 1999.*

Each site poses specific, often ongoing, problems to those who are charged with lighthouse building and upkeep. While the lighthouse's *raison d'être* is to help counter the conditions of weather, waves, currents and natural formations that dictated the need for it in the first place, these very conditions usually hinder its construction and maintenance. In fact, it often seems that the forces of nature are hell-bent on destroying the world's lighthouses—whether by violent extremes of surf, wind and weather, or through the insidious process of erosion and geological shifts. For example, Henry Winstanley, who built Eddystone Rock's first lighthouse on the "wicked reef," off Plymouth, England, was swept away, along with his tower, by storm-driven waves in 1703. Many other lighthouses have suffered a similar fate: to name only two, the first Minots Ledge Light, at Cohasset, Massachusetts, which fell to a tremendous storm in 1851 less than a year after completion; and, more recently, Scotch Cap Lighthouse on Alaska's Unimak Island, which was destroyed by a tsunami in 1946, only six years after its light was first displayed.

The persistent erosion of lighthouse sites by the destructive partnership of wind and waves presents an additional threat to their safety, as seen by the history of the ill-fated Cape Henlopen Lighthouse in Lewes, Delaware. First erected in 1767, it was affected by erosion that was not detected until 1852. All attempts to correct the problem failed, and in 1924 the Lighthouse Service abandoned the struggle and deactivated the lighthouse. Two years later it was finally claimed by the sea, its foundations having been fatally undermined.

Drastic measures are sometimes taken to maintain a light in the face of erosion. The Cape Cod (or Highland) Lighthouse (1798) in Truro, Massachusetts, was replaced with a second tower, set farther back from the sea, in 1857. In 1997 this tower, too, was moved inland. Similarly, the short-term future of one of the best-known American beacons, the Cape Hatteras Lighthouse (1870), was safeguarded in 1999 when the structure was moved from its eroding coastal site in North Carolina.

However, disasters like the one that befell Winstanley's wooden structure at Eddystone can have positive results: the challenges of the site may be reconsidered, and new engineering and construction techniques developed to counter them. In his design for the third Eddystone lighthouse, for instance, engineer John Smeaton corrected the faults that had made his predecessors' structures so vulnerable to the elements. He built a wind-and-wave-resistant foundation and tower (1759) of dovetailed stone, which was also fire-resistant. (Flames had consumed John Rudyerd's 1708 tower on the reef.) Smeaton's lighthouse served successfully until 1882, when it was dismantled because of erosion of the cliff upon which its foundations were anchored.

Sadly, it often proves impossible to preserve a structure whose site is threatened by severe erosion. However, another advance in engineering techniques for site-specific problems is the development of caisson and crib foundations, which provide an effective bulwark against the phenomenal force of moving ice, as seen in the survival of the second Wolf Trap Lighthouse, erected in Chesapeake Bay in 1894. The development of screwpile and caisson construction techniques during the nineteenth century, and the "Texas Tower" configurations of the twentieth, have made it possible to build lighthouses on offshore sites that were once considered impossible.

The constant menace of natural forces means that lighthouse administrations must remain vigilant, monitoring local conditions and structural soundness with great care. This chapter gives a brief overview of some of the problems that they face in so doing.

METEOROLOGICAL AND OCEANOGRAPHIC CONDITIONS

Meteorology is the study of the Earth's atmosphere, and particularly the various processes that result in different types of weather systems. As such, it has special significance for not only sailors (who need to interpret current weather conditions and predict changes that might affect their progress and safe navigation), but also for those who are responsible for constructing, maintaining and operating the navigational aids worldwide. In identifying persistent maritime trouble-spots, and the consequent provision of navigational aids, lighthouse authorities must understand the causes of meteorological conditions affecting each site and surrounding waters and the best ways to ensure that the light remains operational and maximally useful in all anticipated conditions. Without today's advantages of radio shipping forecasts and high-tech meteorological and navigational equipment, not to mention the legacy of centuries of scientific study, it is difficult to imagine how sailors and early lighthouse builders coped with the unpredictability of the weather. Indeed, tragically, many of them did not, forfeiting their lives, and their lighthouses, to the winds, waves and ice.

WINDS

A simplified explanation of Isaac Newton's laws of motion shows that if an external force acts upon a particle, the previously stable particle will change its motion and move at increasing speed toward the force that has attracted and activated it. Newton's laws of motion are an important basis for understanding how winds and waves arise.

Two main storm belts affect the world's seas and oceans: the upper westerlies of temperate latitudes and the tropical-cyclone tracks of equatorial latitudes. Westerlies are prevailing winds that blow from the west, on the poleward sides of the latitudes 30°N and 35°S in winter and 35°N and 30°S in summer, often whipping up storms. In order to qualify as a storm, a wind must reach level 10 (48 to 55 knots) on the Beaufort Scale. It is classified as a violent storm when it reaches 11 (56 to 63 knots) and as a hurricane when it reaches 12 (more than 63 knots). Storms are created when central atmospheric pressure drops from its average figure of 1,000 millibars to a figure of perhaps 960 millibars, the collision of the sharply differing temperatures of the air and the sea's surface generating hurricane-force winds on the westerlies' cold side.

Right: *The red flags to the left of this lighthouse on Grand Cayman are shown here as they warned islanders of the impending landfall of Hurricane Gilbert in 1988.*

Above: The lighthouse at Elbow Cay Reef, on Great Abaco, one of the Bahama Islands. The Bahamas are subject to hurricane-force storms, which can devastate manmade structures and natural features alike.

Tropical cyclones—which are also called hurricanes in the United States, cyclones in the Bay of Bengal and typhoons in the Pacific—are centers of low atmospheric pressure (or depressions, caused by warm, moist air rising upward into cooler conditions, prompting it to condense and release latent heat). Around such depressions, winds spiral inward with great intensity, often attaining speeds of 75 to 200 miles (120 to 320 kilometers) per hour. The tempest created around the still eye of the storm is small, but intensely powerful. Tropical cyclones arise only in the sea (they lose their momentum over land), typically occur in the summer or fall and travel westward. If, for example, they originate in the Atlantic, they speed toward the U.S. East Coast and the West Indies; if they originate in the mid- to western Pacific, they race toward the Philippines, the China Sea and Japan. Tropical cyclones include cumulonimbus clouds, which are also responsible for generating waterspouts—fast-moving funnels of circulating wind that draw sea water up the base of their columns. Waterspouts are weaker than their onshore equivalents, tornadoes, and they cause less damage to vessels and lighthouses. Tornadoes rarely destroy lighthouses, but it has occurred, as in the case of North Carolina's lighthouse dating from 1794 on Bald Head Island, Cape Fear River, in 1812.

The hurricane that battered the coast of Florida in 1846 was so devastating that it is still remembered today. The lighthouses of the island chain called the Florida Keys are constructed on sandy beaches, as at Sand Key, where the first lighthouse was built in 1827, only to collapse in 1846, when hurricane-driven waves washed away the sand that supported it and the stone tower collapsed. (Nearby Key West's 1825 lighthouse suffered a similar fate during the same hurricane.) I.W.P. Lewis and George Meade used screw-pile construction techniques for the replacement skeleton lighthouse of 1853. The tower withstood the fury of another devastating hurricane in 1865, but the key itself was virtually swept away (it has since re-formed). The lighthouse still stands, despite a fire in the keeper's dwelling in 1989.

The Anatomy of a Hurricane

The largest storms on Earth are known by various names. In the Atlantic Ocean, Caribbean Sea and eastern Pacific, the name "Hurricane" probably originated from the Caribbean Indian storm god *Huracan*. In the western Pacific, the name is "Typhoon" from the Chinese word *ty-fung*, meaning "big wind." These same storms in the Indian Ocean or Bay of Bengal are simply known as "Cyclones." The names may change, but the anatomy of these monster storms is universal. The rotation of the Earth, heat from the sun and the energy stored in the warm waters of the tropical oceans all come together to create a massive, spiraling cluster of thunderstorms that can stretch more than 600 miles across and push 60,000 feet up into the atmosphere.

The recipe for hurricane development includes the key ingredients of: (1) warm ocean water (80°F, or 27°C); (2) cooler air aloft over the warm ocean; (3) little, if any, change in wind speed or direction upward through the atmosphere; (4) a convergence of low-level winds; and (5) some atmospheric spin provided by the rotation of the Earth itself. Where these key ingredients are found, thunderstorms begin to develop. Within these thunderstorms, warm, moist air over the ocean is forced upward. As the air rises, it cools and the moisture condenses. The process of condensation releases latent heat, which warms the air again, allowing it to rise still farther. The upward-moving air is replaced near the surface with more warm, moist air from a seemingly endless supply over the vast tropical-ocean surface. The heat released from the condensation of moist air is the fuel that runs a hurricane. Under these conditions the cluster of thunderstorms begins to merge into an organized storm, rotating counterclockwise in the northern hemisphere, or clockwise south of the equator. Once the sustained winds rotating around the center of the storm reach 39mph (63kph) the storm is classified as a "tropical storm" and given a name. When the sustained winds reach 74mph (119kph) the storm is officially a hurricane. If the infant storm remains in ideal atmospheric conditions, it can grow at a phenomenal rate. In September 1983, the winds of Typhoon Forrest in the Pacific Ocean increased from 75mph (121kph) to 173mph (279kph) in just 24 hours!

A mature hurricane is a truly awesome display of atmospheric power: some estimates of the energy released by a single storm are on the order of several hundred hydrogen bombs. In a single day, a mature hurricane can expend enough energy to provide the United States with all the power it needs for an entire week. While hurricanes are perhaps best known for their winds, which may reach speeds of nearly 200mph (322kph), their intensity is actually measured by the barometric pressure at the center of the storm. A low central air pressure is an indication of how efficiently the storm is lifting air away from the surface and up into the atmosphere. The most intense hurricane to hit the United States was the Florida Keys Hurricane of September 1935. Formed before hurricanes were given official names in the 1950s, the center of that storm passed over Matacumbe Key, Florida, with a barometric pressure reading of 26.35 inches. Hurricane Camille, which hit the Gulf coast of the United States in 1969, was nearly as intense with a barometric pressure of 26.84 inches. The most intense storm on record was a nasty Pacific Typhoon named Tip, whose central pressure dropped to an astonishingly low 25.69 inches on October 12, 1979, while winds near the center raged at 190 mph (306kph).

But the infamous wind is only one part of the destructive force associated with hurricanes. Perhaps the most deadly facet of a hurricane is the amount of water it moves around. Estimated to be able to produce up to 20 billion tons of rain water in a single day, a landfalling hurricane can bring much-needed water to drought-stricken areas, or totally swamp a region with devastating floods. When Tropical Cyclone Denise moved through La Reunion Island in the Indian Ocean in January 1966, the result was an almost unbelievable torrent of 71.8 inches (182.4 centimeters) of rain in 24 hours. Fourteen years later, in January 1980, the same tiny island had to endure a ten-day onslaught from Tropical Cyclone Hyacinthe, which produced a mind-boggling total of 223.5 inches (567.7 centimeters) of rain!

Flooding rains combined with a wall of water, pushed onshore by the winds on the forward side of the storm, create the major source of damage and loss of life associated

Cape Florida Light and its surroundings after Hurricane Andrew, 1992.

with hurricane landfall. The wall of water, or "storm surge," can be literally inescapable. Reports of a mound of water 42 feet (13 meters) high were noted for a cyclone that hit Bathurst Bay, Australia, in 1899. A storm surge of 40 feet (12 meters) is estimated to have killed some 300,000 people when a cyclone hit Bangladesh in 1970. In the United States, the coastal topography is not quite as conducive to extreme storm surges. Still, Hurricane Hugo had a storm surge of 20 feet (6 meters) when it crashed into Isle of Palms, South Carolina, in 1989. To fully understand the danger of such surges, it is helpful to note that a cubic foot of seawater weighs about 64 pounds. Thus, a storm surge of 20 feet pushes about 1,280 pounds of seawater onto every cubic foot it covers. Strong enough to totally demolish buildings and roads and even to change the topography of barrier islands. The deadliest weather disaster in the United States was the hurricane that swallowed Galveston Island, Texas, on September 8, 1900. The Galveston hurricane had a storm surge that pushed tides to 15 feet (5 meters) with waves on top of the surge breaking more than 25 feet (8 meters) above normal mean sea level. The hurricane took at least 8,000 lives; most drowned or were crushed as houses and buildings were simply leveled by the storm surge. Those who survived included 125 townspeople who found refuge in the low-lying island's sturdy Bolivar Point Lighthouse.

Hurricanes can strike every continent except Antarctica, where the icy waters prevent tropical-storm formation. It has been estimated that at least 15 percent of the world's population lives near hurricane-prone shorelines. In the United States, some 50 million people live in areas of potential hurricane disaster. These areas are under the gun for half the year, with the hurricane season for the Atlantic Ocean and Gulf of Mexico running from June 1 through November. In the Atlantic basin, an average year will feature about ten storms strong enough to be named—having winds of at least 39mph—and roughly half of those will reach hurricane strength—winds of at least 74mph. Worldwide, an average year brings eighty-four named storms, of which about forty-five will reach hurricane status.

Even hurricanes that never make landfall can disrupt human activity. Large storms that sweep strong winds over many miles

SAFFIR-SIMPSON HURRICANE SCALE

Category	Winds	Central Pressure/Storm Surge	Damage
1.	74–95mph 119–153kph	28.94in or higher/4–5 feet 73.5cm or higher/1.2–1.5 meters	Minimal
2.	96–110mph 154–177kph	28.50–28.93in/6–8 feet 72.39–73.48cm/1.8–2.4 meters	Moderate
3.	111–130mph 178–209kph	27.91–28.49in/9–12 feet 70.89–72.36cm/2.7–3.7 meters	Extensive
4.	131–155mph 210–250kph	27.17–27.90in/13–18 feet 69.01–70.87cm/4–5.5 meters	Extreme
5.	155mph + 250kph +	27.16in or less/18 feet + 68.97cm or less/5.5 meters +	Catastrophic

of ocean water can generate waves in the open ocean of 100 feet (30 meters) or higher. Large swells continue on toward faraway shorelines and rip currents make swimming extremely dangerous. For ships trying to navigate the oceans during hurricane season, the going, obviously, can be very rough. In 1990 the battering 30-foot (9-meter) waves of Hurricane Bertha destroyed a Greek freighter. Modern weather-tracking satellites and radar enable most ships to avoid the worst parts of hurricanes, but that depends on accurate forecasts, which with hurricanes can be an adventure unto itself.

The root of the challenge of forecasting hurricanes lies in the area in which they form. The tropics, when compared to mid-latitudes of the world, are an area where there is little change in temperature from night to day, from east to west or north to south, and from season to season. The lack of a temperature gradient leads to weaker upper level winds, which are the steering currents of the atmosphere, and to generally weaker and more diffuse daily weather systems. In addition, there is a natural data void over the oceans where few surface weather stations exist. Meteorologists forecasting the weather in the tropics pay attention to every subtle change in the analyzed weather. A seemingly insignificant weather disturbance may begin to feed on the enormous supply of warm, moist air in the region and develop to become the next blossoming hurricane.

Once formed, the hurricane is no easier to forecast. The weak upper-level winds that help the storm to maintain its form and gain strength in the first days of development give little indication as to where it will move next. At times a simple extrapolation of the movement from the last few hours can become the best forecast for the future. Advancements in weather-satellite technology, sophisticated computer models and the valuable data received from hurricane hunter planes flying into the storms have greatly improved hurricane forecasting. Lives are being saved by better forecasts and the ability to track the movement of hurricanes and warn people well in advance of their arrival. The days of being blind-sided by a killer hurricane with a death toll in the thousands, like the Galveston disaster of 1900, are behind us. Now the death toll from the worst hurricanes to hit the United States, such as Andrew and Hugo, is down to a few dozen.

Still, a 72-hour forecast of a hurricane's position may be off by hundreds of miles, and not even a perfect forecast would change the fact that these swirling masses of wind and water will continue to visit coastlines that become more developed each year. Future storms will make their headlines in dollars, not deaths. Considering the fact that Hurricane Andrew caused $26 billion in damages when it swept across south Florida in 1992, a $100 billion storm seems likely in the not-too-distant future.

—Tom Tasselmyer,

Chief Meteorologist, WBAL-TV/RADIO, Baltimore, Maryland

WAVES

The height and force of waves are typically determined by the strength, speed, duration, direction and fetch (the distance traveled uninterruptedly over water) of the wind, as well as the position of the land in relation to the sea. As the wind blows across the sea, the friction created between the moving air and water surface generates waves—in effect, the wind transfers its energy to the waves. If the wind is low, waves may appear to be the merest of disturbances on the surface, but in the case of gale-force winds, the energy may drive the water particles comprising the wave into a pattern of frenzied rotation, each particle transmitting its energy to the next, causing crests and troughs, as well as waves of increasing velocity and length. Once whipped up by the wind, such progressive waves may travel great distances on their own energy, even if the wind above them has dropped. Both winds and waves are stronger at sea than over land. On approaching the shore and shallower water, where the potential for vertical movement is restricted by the sea bed, the rotational orbit of the wave's water particles is broken by the resultant friction. Thus the wave's crest moves backward horizontally and its trough forward. This wavelength compression results in the trough losing volume and its crest breaking, whereupon the crest of the succeeding wave overtakes it. A wave will usually break when the depth of the water is half the length of the wave and when the wave's height reaches a tenth of its length. The height of the tallest recorded wave was measured at 111 feet (34 meters), between the Philippines and California, in February 1933.

Waves break more severely on rocky headlands, promontories and islands than on straight coastlines, because instead of approaching them head-on, in a less-forceful formation, waves bend around their irregular forms. This is why such massive headlands as South Africa's Cape of Good Hope and Chile's Cape Horn are notorious for their storm waves. A number of light towers have been erected on both capes, including Cape Agulhas Light (1849), on South Africa's southernmost point, and Chile's isolated Islote Evangelistas Lighthouse (1896).

Countless lighthouses have succumbed to the devastating force of powerful waves, including the first beacon on Bishop's Rock,

Below: Where turbulent seas and high winds are frequent, lighthouses are often built on headlands and cliffs, out of reach of high water. The lighthouse at Scrabster, near Scotland's northeasternmost point, serves traffic between the mainland and the remote Orkney Islands.

Opposite: Bodie Island Light, North Carolina (see gatefold feature).

Below: *Cape Agulhas Light, built in 1848, is South Africa's second oldest. It is located on the Cape of Good Hope, the continent's southernmost tip, where mariners have for several centuries come to grief in the region's legendary storms.*

a granite formation 7 miles (11 kilometers) south of Britain's Scilly Isles. It took engineers four years to construct an iron tower 94 feet (29 meters) tall on this exposed rock, but their efforts were in vain, for shortly after its completion in 1850, a storm swept the lighthouse into the sea. Lessons were learned from this disaster, and a stone cofferdam foundation ensured that the replacement lighthouse of 1858 was better able to resist all that the sea could throw at it.

Tidal waves may be generated by tremors that occur on the sea bed, with the consequent shock waves dispersing outward and upward for long distances. Tidal waves may also be formed by a drop in atmospheric pressure that causes the sea level to rise, and producing waves that travel in the direction of the moving center of depression, whipped up by the circulating winds. Many lighthouses have been destroyed by tidal waves, including Canada's Egg Island Lighthouse (1898), which stood at the entrance to Fitzhugh Sound until 1948. Not only can the sea level rise dramatically, but if there is also a high tide, and torrential rain, a storm surge may result. Such surges threaten onshore lighthouses, like that of the German island of Neuwerk, off the Elbe Estuary (although this lighthouse has not only survived the region's storm surges, but provided safe flood shelter for the island's residents).

In the event of a submarine earthquake or volcanic eruption, a tsunami (a seismic surface wave) may be generated that can travel at a speed of more than 805 miles

Works Always in Progress: Storm Power

Above: In the Bahama Islands, storm-driven waves batter the site of the Great Inagua Lighthouse, which stands in the tropical-cyclone path of the equatorial latitudes—one of the two major storm belts affecting the world's seas and oceans. *Previous page:* The lighthouse on Bodie Island, North Carolina (1872), is the third on this site, which is vulnerable to the sudden hurricane-force storms that plague the Outer Banks. The island's topography is continuously reshaped by the action of the prevailing winds and Atlantic Ocean waves. *Below:* A torrential rainstorm drenches one of the fifteen Cook Islands, an archipelago in Polynesia, whipping up severe gale-force winds in this photo. This part of the South Pacific is prone to typhoons (see feaure, page 28), with winds that wreak havoc on natural and manmade structures alike.

Pacific Surf and a Vulnerable Coastline

This sweeping panorama shows the ocean surf as a storm clears at sunset off Yaquina Head, near Newport, Oregon. The lonely light stands sentinel on the promontory above the bay. The dramatic Pacific coastline of North America has been sculpted by both eons of wave erosion and frequent seismic upheavals caused by the convergence of tectonic and oceanic continental plates. The world's largest and deepest ocean, which is bounded by a chain of volcanoes known as the "Pacific Ring of Fire," is prone to the devastating tsunamis that have claimed both lives and lighthouses. Earthquakes whose epicenters are on land, as well as seismic tremors, constantly alter the Pacific coastline, causing California in particular to be plagued by rock falls and landslides.

The enormous power of the waves, whose passage across the Pacific is virtually unimpeded until they reach North America's West Coast, assaults the coastline and has, over time, caused the erosion of many lighthouse sites. Mariners attempting to navigate this dangerous coast face the challenge of this majestic surf and must be aware of the countless offshore reefs that threaten their vessels. A further treacherous feature of North America's "Dragon Coast" is the frequent occurrence of dense advection fog.

Yaquina Head Light was once known as the Cape Foulweather Light, after the site for which it was originally intended, several miles to the north. The landing of its construction materials at the wrong point may be explained by the vein of magnetized iron ore that runs through the local cliffs, playing havoc with compass bearings. The light's early name was apt: its construction was hindered by fierce storms. Since its completion in 1873, however, the 93-foot (28.3-meter) tower—Oregon's tallest—has guided fog-bound sailors through Yaquina Head's turbulent waters and away from the reefs that threaten their safety.

It is telling that California's Point Bonita (right) was the first lighthouse on the West Coast to be equipped with a fog signal (a cannon) on its completion in 1855. The original light and fog signal proved inadequate aids for vessels entering San Francisco's Golden Gate Straits, however, since low-lying clouds and fog simply enshrouded them. In 1877 a new light was built (shown here) at a point of lower elevation, 124 feet (37.8 meters) above sea level, but with this exposed site came new problems: erosion and landslides, the most serious of which crushed the bridge linking the light-tower and fog-signal building during the 1940s. Reached by a suspension bridge, the lighthouse still stands, although it is probably just a matter of time before the Pacific waves succeed in undermining its foundations.

Wave Erosion

Above: An ominous storm closes in on Mendocino, California, bringing powerful waves that crash over the treacherous rock-studded coastline. *Below:* Relentlessly pounding waves, which break more severely on irregular coastlines, assault the infrastructure of this Sonoma County lighthouse in northern California. Most lighthouses along the Pacific Coast are situated on headlands, well above the reach of destructive storm surf.

Overleaf: Ar-Men Light, which is located off the coast of Brittany, northwestern France, was constructed on fully exposed manmade foundations: both the tower itself and the supporting foundations must resist the incursion of the turbulent waters of the Atlantic Ocean. This aerial view (© Jean Guichard 1989, AlphaPix) clearly illustrates the success of the engineers' design for the rapid escape of wave swells.

MEN

(continued from page 32)

(500 kilometers) per hour at a relatively low height of 1 foot 6 inches (0.5 meters)—that is, until its progress is slowed on approaching land, when its height can rise to over 100 feet (30 meters), devastating everything in its path. Indeed, the highest recorded tsunami, observed in 1771, was estimated to peak at a towering 280 feet (85 meters). The name "tsunami" is derived from the Japanese words *tsu*, meaning "port," and *nami*, "wave," attesting to its prevalence in Japanese waters due to earthquake activity. Indeed, many of Japan's lighthouses have been reinforced with steel and prestressed concrete to withstand earthquakes. California, another region plagued by seismic activity, lost its Santa Barbara Light, which had stood since 1856, to an earthquake in 1925. The foundations of Cape Hinchinbrook's first lighthouse (1910), on Alaska's Hinchinbrook Island, at the entrance to Prince William Sound, were so badly damaged by earthquakes in 1927–28 that the weakened structure was abandoned and a new lighthouse built on a less vulnerable, rocky site nearby. The second Cape Hinchinbrook lighthouse was completed in 1934.

Below: The Pacific surf pounds the rocky coastline of Vancouver Island, British Columbia, making the surrounding waters hazardous to navigate. Shown here is the lonely Lennard Island Light, with treacherous rocks in the foreground.

Right: Dense fog shrouds these sheer slopes near Bodo, Norway.

Opposite: Coquille River Lighthouse, Bandon, Oregon, in limited visibility. Clearly audible fog signals are essential to supplement lights as aids to navigation in fog-prone locations.

FOG

Many lighthouse sites were chosen because they were often fogbound, a dangerous atmospheric condition that can cause mariners to lose their bearings, become disoriented and steer their vessels onto natural hazards. There are two types of fog: radiation and advection. Radiation fog is caused when at night, the Earth releases the heat that it has absorbed from the Sun, which is then cooled rapidly within the atmosphere. Advection fog arises when warm air meets a cold moist surface like sea water, or when two currents of air—one warm, the other cooler—collide. In the case of both radiation and advection fog, the warm air cools and condenses, creating vapor that forms the microscopic droplets of water comprising a fog bank. The thickness of the fog varies according to both the size of the droplets and their density: the tinier and more numerous they are, the

Below: The lighthouse on the Aran Isle of Inisheer, off Western Ireland, where foggy conditions often prevail.

poorer the visibility. The definition of fog, as opposed to mist or haze, is when visibility drops to 1 kilometer (0.6 miles) or less.

Locations that are particularly prone to fog include Britain's North Sea coast, the Grand Banks off Canada's Newfoundland, the northeastern U.S. coast and the Pacific coast of Peru. This is one reason why such lighthouses as Minots Ledge and the Torre Reloj del Muelle de Guerra Lighthouse, in Calloa Harbor, on Peru's Pacific coast (1889), were built. Fog signals often serve as a back-up in the event of really dense fog that obscures the lighthouse's beam. Maine's Whitehead Lighthouse (1852) was once equipped with a bell weighing 2,000 pounds (907 kilograms); its ingenious mechanism sounded it by harnessing the power of the waves. The foghorn at the twin Cape Ann Lights (1861), on Massachusetts' Rockport Island, is credited with saving the life of President Woodrow Wilson and other passengers aboard the S.S. *America.* The ship was returning to the United States after the peace conference at Versailles, France, that concluded World War I, when it was suddenly engulfed in impenetrable fog.

Opposite and below: *The frequent occurrence of fog makes the rocky coastlines of Maine (opposite, Portland Head Light) and Newfoundland (below, Lobster Cove Head Light), whose waters are studded with submerged hazards, even more treacherous to mariners.*

Opposite: *Holland Harbor South Pierhead Light (or "Big Red"), on Lake Michigan, stands on a manmade foundation designed to withstand prolonged exposure to icy conditions during the winter months.*

Overleaf: *The front and rear range lights at Grand Haven, Michigan, are built on a sturdy pier with a steel-and-iron walkway projecting into the lake. This dusk scene shows the entire structure icebound.*

Below: *An aerial view showing the ice that has formed offshore and the lighthouse at Cheticamp, Nova Scotia.*

ICE

Ice is a particular problem in such northerly climes as North America's five freshwater Great Lakes and the St. Lawrence Seaway that flows from the Gulf of St. Lawrence, on the Atlantic coast, to the St. Louis River in Minnesota. The Great Lakes and the St. Lawrence are often icebound during the winter, and the lighthouses of these waterways are vulnerable to ice even when navigation shuts down for the winter. The Great Lakes are also subject to violent and unpredictable weather conditions like storms and blizzards, as well as impenetrable fog banks and gales, caused by the collision of Arctic and southern fronts over these vast expanses of water. During the four years (1870–74) required to construct the crib-foundation lighthouse at Spectacle Reef, at the junction of Lakes Huron and Michigan on the Straits of Mackinac, work had to stop every winter. On the workmen's return in spring 1874, they found the lighthouse surrounded by an icy shroud 30 feet (9 meters) high, which had to be forcibly cleared before work could be resumed. It is moving ice, however, that presents an even more significant threat to the lighthouse, and countries that endure Arctic conditions, like Finland and Iceland, have had to safeguard their lighthouses from the pressure of collisions.

Freshwater ice is formed when temperatures fall below 32°F (0°C), and sea ice, when temperatures of about 28.5°F (-1.91°C) and lower are reached. The water freezes to form six-sided crystalline structures (which, in the case of sea water, are called frazil ice), which build up rapidly through coalescence. Ice floes occur either when chunks of ice break away from a parent ice sheet to form floating icebergs, or ice shelves (as in Chile, Alaska, Antarctica and New Zealand, for example); or when sea water freezes, the latter being the usual threat to lighthouses. Ice floats because it is less dense than water; when you consider that sea water freezes to an average thickness of 8 feet 2 inches (2.5 meters), and that it is propelled by the strength of powerful waves and currents, even an apparently immovable lighthouse may succumb to these irresistible forces. This fate befell Virginia's twenty-three-year-old Wolf Trap lighthouse in Chesapeake Bay in 1870, and Maryland's ten-year-old Hooper Strait Light, also in Chesapeake Bay, in 1877.

HYDROGRAPHIC AND GEOLOGICAL CONSIDERATIONS

A lighthouse site may comprise such geomorphical features as rocks, cliffs, barriers and reefs, and in order to understand the problems associated with construction on these varied foundations, and the dangers they pose to mariners, it is necessary to explore their structure and composition.

Rocks and cliffs (precipitous rock faces ranged along the shoreline) constitute part of the Earth's crust, and are classified into three types: igneous, sedimentary and metamorphic. Igneous rocks, which were formed by the cooling of magma (molten rock), include granite and basalt, both of which are hard. Sedimentary rocks are made up of layers of organic or mineral components that have built up through the movement of water, wind, or glacial ice. Metamorphic rocks (which may originally have been igneous and sedimentary) are those whose composition has changed through the action of heat or pressure, sedimentary shale, for example, being metamorphosed into slate. Rocks and cliffs rise high above the sea, making them prime candidates for lighthouses that need elevated sites. The world's highest cliffs are the 3,314-foot (1,010-meter) giants on Hawaii's Molokai Island, where a lighthouse with a tower 138 feet (42 meters) tall was built in 1909 to alert ships to the fringe reef (a coral reef) that encompasses the island.

The dangers faced by early engineers of lighthouses on isolated, wave-swept rocks seem unimaginably daunting today, and their efforts heroic, whether or not they succeeded, or, indeed, survived. One rock-foundation lighthouse built with great difficulty was St. George Light, designed to warn vessels away from the dangerous reefs off Point St. George, just north of Crescent City, on California's northwest coast. Although work began in 1883 with the slow process of carving a foundation from Seal Rock—whose diameter was only 300 feet (91 meters)—the lighthouse did not go into operation until 1892, partly because the necessary funds from Congress were not forthcoming. Progress was also delayed by waves, which often swept precut blocks of granite weighing 3.5 tons (3,556 kilograms) into the sea, completely damaging work and taking a construction worker's life. The dangers of this exposed site remained tragically evident even after the lighthouse went into operation. Three Coast Guardsmen drowned in 1951 when their shore-bound boat capsized.

***Above:** The Rock of Gibraltar, a narrow limestone peninsula, strategically guards the western entrance to the Mediterranean Sea. Trinity Light stands atop the cliffs of Gibraltar's southernmost extremity, Europa Point.*

***Opposite:** Nawiliwili Bay on the Hawaiian island of Kauai, with black volcanic rock clearly visible in the foreground and the lighthouse standing sentinel on a headland.*

***Below:** Cape Lookout Lighthouse stands at the southern end of North Carolina's notorious Outer Banks, justly known as the "Graveyard of the Atlantic." Lighthouses on these low-lying islands must achieve towering heights, and engineers must contend with the fact that the foundations are constantly compromised by wave erosion.*

Ultimately, the lighthouse was replaced by a large navigational buoy, in 1975.

Barriers, as well as barrier islands and sandbars, are usually created by the action of breaking waves on the bedrock, which, through the action of longshore currents, may build up sand or shingle beaches, spits, islands and offshore bars that are parallel to the coast. Although they perform a useful function in protecting the coastline from waves, barriers may also present an obstacle, and hence a hazard, to the mariner, particularly if they are submerged and invisible to the naked eye. A notorious sandbar lies at the mouth of the Columbia River, on which countless vessels had been wrecked while negotiating the river to and from the Pacific. A lighthouse was clearly required, and the site selected was Washington State's nearby Cape Disappointment. Underlining the need for the lighthouse, during its construction in 1853 the supply vessel *Oriole* foundered on the bar, delaying work on the structure, which was finally lit in 1856. Another hazard of these barriers is their tendency to migrate onshore, a phenomenon caused by the direction and energy of the wind and waves that is generally the result of longshore drift.

Attempts have often been made to build lighthouses on some of the world's treacherous offshore shoals. Although the odds against them have been awesome, many such ventures have succeeded. Others have not, as seen in the unsuccessful attempt to build a lighthouse on Trinity Shoals, 20 miles (32 kilometers) off the Louisiana coast in the Gulf of Mexico. During the storm-plagued construction project in 1873, first a supply ship, the *Guthrie,* foundered on the shoals, and then the laboriously built workmen's platform was swept out to sea. This dangerous venture was abandoned in favor of a lightship, which took up its duties in 1881.

One of the world's most perilous chains of barrier islands is the Outer Banks, off the coast of North Carolina. South of here, the warm northbound waters of the Gulf Stream collide with the cold southbound waters of the Labrador Current, causing turbulent seas. The threat to sailors is compounded by the shallow rocks of the Diamond Shoals that lie 15 miles (24 kilometers) off the Outer Banks and extend for 8 miles (13 kilometers) from Cape Hatteras. The area's nickname, the "Graveyard of the Atlantic," is a grim testament to the

number of mariners' lives (an estimated 2,300) that it has claimed. Its first lighthouse was erected by Henry Dearborn at Cape Hatteras in 1803. Even though it was 95 feet (30 meters) tall, it was often obscured by mist, its light insufficiently visible from the Diamond Shoals. The Lighthouse Board's investigative committee reported in 1851 that there was "no light on the entire coast of the United States of greater value to the commerce and navigation of the country" and simultaneously damned it as the "worst light in the world." In 1853 the tower was raised to a height of 150 feet (46 meters), and a Fresnel lens was installed, which functioned effectively until the American Civil War intervened. The second lighthouse at Cape Hatteras was completed in 1870; at a height of 193 feet (59 meters), it was—and remains—the tallest in the United States. Over the following decades, however, it was not war, but erosion caused by storm waves, that threatened the granite foundations of this essential lighthouse. In 1936 the Bureau of Lighthouses constructed a skeleton tower 1 mile (2.6 kilometers) farther inland to assume the duties of the station. The old tower was deemed safe to relight in 1950, but by 1999, it was in imminent danger of toppling into the sea. It was physically removed from its site at a multimillion-dollar cost to preserve it.

The dramatic history of the Cape Hatteras Light is one of the most notable examples of the insidious, ongoing threat that erosion poses to those who battle to keep the world's lighthouses functioning safely and efficiently.

Above: *Black Head Light, in western Ireland's County Clare, stands on a promontory overlooking Galway Bay at the edge of a distinctive limestone formation known as The Burren. Limestone is particularly prone to erosion, so this beacon is set back from the cliff edge.*

Opposite: *The rugged sandstone cliff face, showing horizontal erosion patterns, below the lighthouse at Point Conception, California.*

EROSION AND DEPOSITION

Even when coastlines are not subjected to the fury of destructive storms, the constant action of the tides and waves lapping against them can generate sufficient energy, and concomitant hydraulic pressure, to erode lighthouse sites. In addition, winds can transform and threaten the site by shifting tons of sand. Indeed, the coastline can be described as the battle zone between land and sea, with waves either eroding the coastline relentlessly or, through deposition, altering it adversely. In the former case, the backwash of destructive waves removes sections of the shore; in the latter, the swash of constructive waves gradually deposits sediment upon it.

Hydraulic shock, the process by which erosion most commonly occurs, is created when either water or air are compressed at the vanguard of a wave, causing a concentrated hammering effect against the rock or cliff, which is compounded by the negative pressure built up as the water or air retreats, causing the compressed air to "explode." Fissures, or hairline fractures, in rocks—their weakest points—are especially vulnerable to the force of this compressive stress. Through their explosive widening, the mass of which they are a part may become unstable and eventually collapse—a process that is called cavitation.

In the case of rocky sites, a form of erosion known as attrition may be caused by the friction and, as a result, abrasion, generated by the action of waves on the rock, particularly when particles of sand or shingle are also present. A related form of rock erosion, corrasion, may occur when wind, waves, or ice transport fragments of rock or pebbles over the rock or cliff at such a level of pressure that the surface of the original rock is slowly, but surely, scraped away. Cliffs are on the front line of this sustained onslaught, the base being the first area to show signs of erosion. Ultimately, the cliff may be undercut and destabilized to the extent that the overhanging rock collapses, all that remains being a wave-cut, or abrasion, platform at the bottom of the cliff. Some of the many lighthouses that have fallen victim to erosion over the centuries include the various incarnations of the Chatham Light on Cape Cod, Massachusetts. The twin wooden towers that were first erected high on a sandy cliff here in 1808 had to be replaced by brick towers during the 1830s; they stood until further erosive action caused them to collapse into the sea. They were replaced in 1877 by a pair of cast-iron structures built on a less vulnerable site in Chatham's harbor. Only the northern structure still remains, its southern counterpart having been transported to Nauset Beach in 1923.

Below: *A lonely lighthouse stands atop this sheer, fissured granite cliff at Southwest Head, Grand Manan Island, New Brunswick.*

1881

Biological weathering, another form of rock erosion, results when rock-boring mollusks penetrate the formation, sometimes causing total disintegration. Solution weathering occurs when high levels of carbon monoxide in the air, sea water, or acid rain, dissolve the minerals contained within chalk and limestone rocks. The dramatic effects of solution can be seen on the chalky island of Rügen, in Germany, on whose northern cape, Arkona, successive lighthouses were built in 1827 and 1902. Rocks may also be weathered by frost, as well as by the salt in sea water.

Longshore drift may erode beaches and add to neighboring shores. This phenomenon occurs when longshore currents (which run parallel or oblique to the coast) shift and then deposit the sediment that makes up a beach (such as sand or shell debris, pebbles, or even rocks that have broken off from the land or bedrock through erosion) further along the shore. At Dungeness, Kent, on England's southeastern coast, longshore drift has necessitated the construction of three lighthouses at separate locations. The original light tower, which was built in 1615 on the tip of a spit, was replaced by another in 1635, by which time longshore drift had caused an accretion of shingle to the extent that the first lighthouse was set significantly back from the shore. The 1635 lighthouse was superseded by a new structure built by Samuel Wyatt in 1792, which stood firm until 1904, when it became necessary to demolish the upper section. Unusually, its replacement was not rendered redundant by the sea, but by the giant towers of the power station that was built nearby later in the twentieth century, which blocked its light from passing ships. The lighthouse that guides ships today was erected in 1959; since 1962 it has been floodlit at night to prevent the birds that inhabit this nature reserve from flying into it. It is sometimes possible to control severe cases of longshore drift by building groins, or barriers, at right angles to the prevailing direction of the longshore currents, which serve to reduce the force of the waves that reach the shore.

Shifting offshore sands pose another threat to the safety of sailors. These sands are covered by the sea at high tide, but when the tide ebbs, they are exposed to the air and dry out until they have hardened. When they are submerged again at high tide, the sands soften, shift and reassemble at a new location unknown to the mariner. The Goodwin

Below: *A series of pilings protects the shore of the seaside resort of Ahrenshoop, in the state of Mecklenburg-West Pomerania, on Germany's northern coast. The Baltic Sea that bounds this low-lying area is notable for both its shallowness and low levels of salinity, with the result that it may be icebound for up to five months of the year. The region's cliffs are comprised of soft chalk, which is relatively soluble and readily eroded by sea water.*

Above: Erosion protection pilings in front of Currituck Light, a conical brick structure on North Carolina's fragile Outer Banks.

Sands, which lie 3 miles (5 kilometers) off the coast of Deal, Kent, in southeastern England, are a notorious example of this phenomenon. Perhaps unsurprisingly, it has proved impossible to build a lighthouse on this site, and today three lightships, as well as numerous buoys, alert mariners to the dangers that they pose. The advantage of these aids to navigation is that their position can be adjusted to reflect the movement of the sands. (There are a number of intriguing legends associated with the Goodwin Sands, one of which maintains that they were once a fertile island owned by Earl Godwin—the father of the King Harold who met his end at the Battle of Hastings—which was submerged by an act of God when Earl Godwin broke his vow to take communion every day.)

In other regions it is the shifting of mud that may create a navigational hazard, as seen at the mouth of the Mississippi River, which is appropriately nicknamed the Big Muddy. Obeying a principle similar to that which causes longshore drift, silt, sand and other forms of marine debris tend to build up there and rot into glutinous mud, which is shifted around the Mississippi Delta. Louisiana's grandiose marble-and-granite Franks Island Lighthouse, which was designed by Benjamin Latrobe (the architect responsible for raising the Capitol, in Washington, D.C.), fell to the mud shortly after its erection by Winslow Lewis in 1818. Although its 1823 masonry replacement survives, the foundations have dropped 20 feet (6 meters) below their original level. Similarly, the level of the Pass à L'Outre Light, which assumed the function of the one at Franks Island in 1856, had fallen by 5 feet (1.5 meters) twenty years after completion, as a result of shifting mud. It can still be seen, although its light was decommissioned in 1930 because huge mud deposits had rendered the surrounding waters nearly impassable. It was only with the advent of the "Texas Tower," an oil-rig type of lighthouse exemplified by the Southwest Pass Jetty Light (1965), that the challenge posed by Mississippi mud was overcome.

***Above:** The long breakwater at Schurman's Point, Prince Edward Island, protects the harbor channel from heavy surf.*

***Opposite:** A close-up view of the pier structure leading to Frankfort Lighthouse, Michigan.*

***Overleaf:** The cast-iron and concrete North Pierhead Light and fog signal that guard the entrance to the Sturgeon Bay Ship Canal, Wisconsin, from Lake Michigan.*

MANMADE LIGHTHOUSE SITES

Finally, despite the option of providing an alternative aid to navigation in the form of a lightship or buoy, it is sometimes necessary to create an artificial foundation to support a lighthouse where no suitable site exists, particularly in harbors that have no natural protection from storms and waves. One reason why such successful harbors or ports as those at Hong Kong and New York City have enjoyed the benefits of major marine-based trade is that they are sheltered by islands on the one hand and by shores on the other. No such shelter existed at, for example, Rockland Harbor, Maine, so in 1888 a breakwater was constructed with a light tower at its extremity to guide in approaching vessels. This aid to navigation was improved upon in 1902, when the breakwater was lengthened and a new lighthouse was built on a granite pier at the end.

Other examples of pier lighthouses can be found on the Great Lakes, including Indiana's Michigan City East Pier Light, constructed on concrete foundations in 1904, and Michigan's red South Haven South Pier Lighthouse (1903). Like many pier lighthouses, these towers on the shores of Lake Michigan were clad in steel to improve their resistance to storm and ice damage.

The construction of such artificial lighthouse sites illustrates the ingenuity of the lighthouse builders, and the advances in technical know-how that had been slowly and painfully accumulated, mainly through trial and error. Centuries of expensive—often disappointing—experience had given lighthouse engineers a better understanding of siting, and new modes of construction could enable a given lighthouse to withstand the destructive force of the natural elements that constantly threatened to demolish it.

TRADITIONAL LIGHTHOUSES

Deconstructing the Onshore Lighthouse

Until the eighteenth century, scant consideration was given to the idea of building lighthouses on offshore sites. Indeed, with the advent of such engineering techniques as screwpile and caisson construction as yet undreamed of, any such enterprise would not only have been extremely foolhardy but doomed to disaster. It was not just a lack of technical know-how that restricted most lighthouses to onshore sites (with the exception of some island locations on which purchase could be achieved, like Pharos Island, Alexandria, and Cordouan Island, France), but also common sense. For, as Alan Stevenson, the lighthouse pioneer who made his name with the construction of Scotland's Skerryvore Lighthouse (1844), advised in his work *A Rudimentary Treatise on the History, Construction and Illumination of Lighthouses* (1850): "The most prominent points of a line of coast, or those first made on overseas voyages, should first be lighted...so that they may be discovered by the mariner as long as possible before his reaching land." Land was the mariner's destination, so it made sense to build lighthouses on coastal sites close to the harbors at which trading vessels docked to offload their cargoes. It was principally commercial considerations that dictated the need for lighthouses, and it is no accident that it was the Romans, whose empire's prosperity relied on trade, who built some of the earliest permanent lighthouses at such important ports in their far-flung territories as Dover, in England; Bordeaux, in France; and Ostia, in Italy.

Few such ancient aids to navigation have survived, partly as a result of centuries of neglect or warfare and partly because of the devastation wreaked by the powerful forces of nature on inadequate structures. If they managed to withstand the fury of the winds and waves, wooden towers were frequently ignited by their beacons' naked flames. Although stone structures generally fared

***Previous pages:** Australia's easternmost beacon, Cape Byron Light (1901), stands on a clifftop overlooking Byron Bay, New South Wales. Although the reinforced-concrete tower is only 59 feet (18 meters) tall, its elevated position gives it a focal-plane height of 387 feet (118 meters) above sea level.*

***Left:** North Carolina's Cape Hatteras Light compensates for its low-lying position on a barrier island off the Atlantic coast with its impressive height of 193 feet (59 meters), making it the United States' tallest light tower.*

Below: The red-and-white banded tower of Namibia's Swakopmund Light, in southwestern Africa, soars gracefully into the sky. This low-lying port site, whose hinterland is the Namib Desert, requires an elevated beacon to guide mariners approaching on the Atlantic Ocean.

better, they, too, were threatened by adverse weather and site conditions, whether storms or erosion, as well as by human conflict. Lighthouses have often been caught in the crossfire over the centuries. It was the internecine warfare of the Italian city states during the Middle Ages that caused the destruction in 1290 of Meloria's 1157 lighthouse, and the American Civil War saw Union naval forces damage Alabama's 1822 Mobile Point Light beyond repair in 1864.

During World War II, the medieval lighthouse at Livorno, Italy, succumbed to a similar fate. Unless they were designed to serve as both a fortress and an aid to navigation, builders seldom took defense into consideration when planning their lighthouses.

GENERAL PRINCIPLES OF LIGHTHOUSE CONSTRUCTION

For primary landfall or "making" lighthouses, it is vital that the beam can be seen far out to sea, a requirement that must take into account the curvature of the Earth, which, if the lighthouse is not correctly positioned, can obscure the mariner's view of its light. Therefore, the optimum site for an onshore lighthouse is high on a clifftop, a natural advantage that lessens the need for a tall tower. Thus although South Korea's Komundo Lighthouse, for instance, which guides mariners through the Cheju Strait, is only 21 feet (6.4 meters) tall, its commanding clifftop position gives it a focal-plane height of 266 feet (69 meters). Where there are no cliffs, the lighthouse must be heightened to compensate for its low-lying position. This is why sections of the U.S. southern Atlantic shoreline boast such tall towers as North Carolina's Cape Hatteras Lighthouse, which was erected in 1870 at a height of 193 feet (59 meters), with a focal-plane height of 191 feet (58 meters). In addition, the contours of the lighthouse should minimize potential wind and wave damage as much as possible, which is why a conical or cylindrical form, or variants thereof, are preferable to square towers in regions that are plagued by heavy storms and angry seas.

In ancient days, the lighthouse's beacon of fire was exposed to the elements, a highly unsatisfactory situation that was solved only when the introduction of a wooden enclosure, or lantern, made it infinitely easier to keep the light burning. Reached by means of an interior staircase, the lantern containing the illuminant is usually, but not always, placed at the top of the tower. A notable exception is the lantern room of Ireland's reinforced-concrete Rathlin West Lighthouse (1919), which was constructed at the foot of the structure to reduce the level of the light's elevation and thereby make it a more effective aid to navigation on that fog-bound site. Whatever the lantern room's position, it is encircled by a railed gallery, or walkway, which enables the exterior to be cleaned and maintained. Some lighthouses have an additional level sandwiched between the lantern room and tower, which, before the days of automation, was used as the keeper's watch room and could also be surrounded by a gallery.

Lantern rooms, which may assume a variety of shapes—round, square, or polyhedral—are bounded by glass windows that extend from floor to ceiling, with the illuminant placed centrally. Until the advent of Fresnel lenses, the windows of early "birdcage" lanterns consisted of small glass panes contained in an intricate copper framework. Copper was also used for the dome or peaked roof that surmounted the lantern room, at the center of which a ventilation ball was placed that supported a lightning rod. New lantern-room blueprints were designed during the nineteenth century to house the seven Fresnel-lens orders, with a choice of six, eight, or ten glass sides, one of which was hinged to provide a doorway to the gallery. Cast-iron (and subsequently aluminum) then became the preferred materials for the framework, as they were more durable than copper. Some lanterns have metal bars placed across their glass to reinforce it; in earlier times they conformed to a vertical or horizontal pattern, but during the late nineteenth century a diagonal configuration came to be preferred: it was believed to present less of a visual obstruction to the revolving light beam and to minimize distortion.

Above: Brandaris Light is located on Terschelling Island, one of the three Dutch West Friesian Islands that were formed when the Wadden Sea flooded the sand dunes that bounded them. The flat, low-lying nature of the site dictates an elevated light tower.

There are exceptions to these general construction rules, however, as when less severe weather and site conditions enable some architectural latitude, or when a structure that was not originally built to serve as a lighthouse assumed this function later in its history. The El Morro fortress, for example, built by Puerto Rico's Spanish occupiers at San Juan's harbor entrance in 1539, was first lit in 1853. The defensive tower erected on the German island of Neuwerk during the thirteenth century, despite the lantern that now protrudes from its summit, retains its massive square walls, punctuated by a few small windows designed to repel attackers. Another German lighthouse, the oldest of twelve beacons at

Opposite: *Constructed at the entrance to San Juan's harbor in 1539, Puerto Rico's El Morro Castle was primarily intended as a fortress, only assuming its role as a beacon in 1853. The present elaborately ornamented brick tower dates from 1908.*

Below: *The lighthouse on Puerto Rico's Culebrita Island was constructed in 1885, during the period of Spanish colonial rule. The elements of its masonry construction are clearly visible in this photograph.*

Bremerhaven, resembles a cathedral's ornate spire. Although it is tempting to speculate that its appearance pays tribute to the Dark Age monks who lit beacons in their church towers to aid mariners, the neo-Gothic Bremerhaven Lighthouse of 1854 was designed by an architect who specialized in ecclesiastical buildings: Simon Loschen was also responsible for the north German port's most important church. Despite the disadvantages of the quadrangular shape in terms of wind and wave resistance, numerous square lighthouses dot the world's shores, including that on the Danish island of Baagoe (1816); Finland's Utö Lighthouse, which was rebuilt in 1814 after the destruction of its predecessor of 1735 during the war against Russia in 1809; and the historic Derby Wharf Light in Salem, Massachusetts (1871).

Other lighthouses have been built in variants of the so-called dwelling-house style, in which the tower protrudes from the roof of a low building that houses the keeper's quarters. This popular style is common where the site is elevated or sheltered and for harbor approaches where the light's range need not be very long. Such integrated dwelling-and-tower structures, which are relatively economical to build and maintain, include the lighthouse on Greece's Psittalia Island, in the Saronic Gulf, which was completed in 1856; and the La Rochetta Lighthouse in Venice, Italy, which went into operation in 1850. In the United States, most lighthouses built in this configuration are known as "Cape Cod" lights, after an architectural style of the East Coast region in which they originated, although they were later built on the Pacific Coast. One example is the Point Pinos Lighthouse, near Monterey, California—the West Coast's oldest functioning lighthouse—which was first lit in 1855. In fact, for purposes of bureaucratic convenience, most of the early West Coast lighthouses were of the Cape Cod design, which was devised by the Treasury Department's architect, Ammi B. Young, a native New Englander.

As these examples illustrate, there are no hard-and-fast rules for the design of onshore lighthouses, because their range requirements, sites and the weather conditions to which they are subject are so diverse. What is crucial, however, is that they be constructed soundly and in conformity to the function for which they were designed and the demands of their sites. This chapter highlights the evolution of the techniques and materials that have been employed, with varying degrees of success, in the construction of onshore lighthouses over the centuries.

Opposite: *The Grand Island East Channel Lighthouse, which is situated on Michigan's Upper Peninsula, on Lake Superior, was first lit in 1870. Constructed of timber on a brick foundation, the light was deactivated in 1913.*

TIMBER TOWERS

Towers made of timber were among the first permanent beacons built along the world's coastlines. Their advantages included the ready availability of local wood, speed of construction and low cost. Their primary disadvantage was their impermanence, for not only did many fall to the force of storm winds and waves, but the fire that fueled the beacon was easily fanned by the wind into a raging inferno that consumed the building. Many wooden lighthouses have succumbed to fire, including the first beacon on Alaska's Five Finger Islands (1902), which was reduced to ashes in 1933. As a result of such disasters, many original wooden lighthouses have not survived.

The early history of the second colonial lighthouse built in North America, a conical wooden tower erected in 1746 at Brant Point, Nantucket Island, Massachusetts, illustrates the vulnerability of wooden structures to the elements of fire and water. Having burned to the ground in 1758, its replacement of 1759 was swept away by a "most violent Gust of Wind" in 1774. The third lighthouse here caught fire in 1783, and the fourth (1786) was soon demolished by a storm in 1788. Eventually, a brick tower was erected, in 1856, and although it still stands, its light-giving function was assumed by a wooden tower in 1901 due to the shifting of Nantucket's harbor channel. Unlike its wooden predecessors, this timber lighthouse has survived intact, and still displays its light today (its focal-plane height is the lowest in New England). Similarly, California's Point Cabrillo Lighthouse, whose octagonal timber tower is integrated into a now-defunct fog-signal building, has stood from 1909 to this day, demonstrating that the choice of wood is not necessarily problematic at certain sites and since the advent of safer fuels.

Despite the many threats to their survival, other timber beacons still light the world's coasts, including Norway's Homlungen Lighthouse, on the Hvaler Archipelago, on Oslo Fjord's western shore. Built in the style of a dwelling house, with a lantern and gallery perched on an elevated second story to one side, the wooden lighthouse seen today was constructed in 1915 to replace the original structure of 1867. Similarly, the ornate

Right: *The oldest lighthouse on Canada's Prince Edward Island, Prim Point Light has watched over Hillsborough Bay since 1846. The conical brick tower is clad in a coat of wooden shingles.*

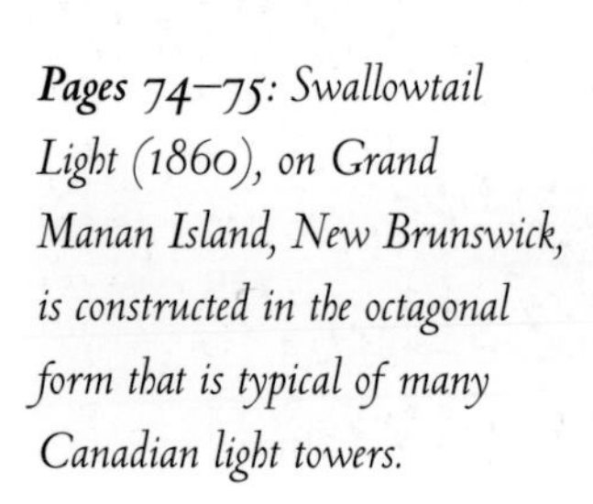

Pages 74–75: *Swallowtail Light (1860), on Grand Manan Island, New Brunswick, is constructed in the octagonal form that is typical of many Canadian light towers.*

A Timber Dwelling-Style Beacon

Hereford Inlet Light, New Jersey

A porch and ornate gallery add charm to this square-towered timber lighthouse, demonstrating the prevailing architectural fashions at the time of its construction in 1874. The light tower is an integral part of the keeper's dwelling, a style commonly adopted for beacons whose light source need not be particularly elevated. Despite the fact that this lighthouse was not designed for an exposed location, it proved durable enough to withstand a devastating hurricane that laid much of the vicinity to waste in 1889, as well as outbreaks of fire. Originally located at the entrance to Hereford Inlet, the beacon's fourth-order Fresnel lens was later replaced with a red-and-white flashing optic. Following its deactivation in 1964, this picturesque lighthouse was moved to the town of North Wildwood, where it can today be admired by the public.

1 *The staircase to the lantern room.*
2 *The lighthouse features a decorative gallery and unusually large windows.*
3 *The red-and-white flashing optic.*

4 *The keeper's office below the gallery level.*
5 *Turning mechanism weights.*
6 *A home from home—the keeper's sleeping quarters.*

GRAND MANAN V

***Below:** Castle Hill Light, near Newport, Rhode Island, was built on foundations cut into the edge of a rocky ridge. In 1890 a beacon was lit atop this 34-foot (10.4-meter) granite rubblestone tower, the durability of its construction enabling it to survive a hurricane in 1938.*

Italianate Point Fermin Light (1874), which was built of California redwood and once stood on Point Fermin, at the entrance to California's San Pedro Harbor, can still be admired at its new parkland site in Los Angeles, although it was decommissioned in 1942. Canada is particularly rich in heavy-beamed wooden towers, including a number on Prince Edward Island, among them those at Blockhouse Point (1851), Seacow Head (1863) and Wood Islands (1876).

MASONRY TOWERS

Masonry (stone or brick) lighthouses proved much more enduring than their timber counterparts. Over time, their initial construction material of rubblestone (roughly broken stones) gave way to precut or dressed stone, preferably granite, and then brick. Not only was masonry sturdier and more weatherproof than timber, it also allowed for construction of sounder foundations that enabled the lighthouse to withstand storm damage better. In addition, although lantern rooms were still frequently fashioned of wood, a beacon fire rarely spread to the supporting masonry structure unless it incorporated timber elements or cladding.

Erected either directly on bedrock or, where ground was softer, sometimes on wooden, and later iron, piles drilled into the substratum, the foundations were then covered with a wooden cribbage or grillage (a supportive arrangement of beams and crossbeams). Because of the great cumulative weight of the stones or bricks that made up the tower, a rubblestone (usually granite) base, often several feet thick, surmounted the cribbage. The tower then tapered inward as it rose into a conical, octagonal, or pyramidal form. This construction design resulted in an evenness of weight distribution that had been impossible to achieve with wooden towers and hence ensured a far more stable lighthouse. Indeed, it has been retained as the standard foundation structure of most heavy onshore lighthouses, including towers built of cast iron and reinforced concrete.

The stone that was used to build such light towers was usually from a local source. The first lighthouse at Cape Henry, on Virginia Beach, which was completed in 1792, was erected from local sandstone in an octagonal form to a height of 90 feet (27 meters); another sandstone light tower is Macquarie Lighthouse (1817) in Sydney, Australia.

By contrast, local limestone was used in Estonia's ancient Kopu Lighthouse (1531), which was built to Hans Scherer and Klaves Duker's unusual quadrangular design. Limestone was also used for the Point Amour Lighthouse (1857) on Forteau Bay—which, at 118 feet (36 meters), is Canada's second tallest—and for Bermuda's St. David's Lighthouse (1879). Where it was available, a harder rock, such as granite, was preferred for such lighthouses as Chile's Bahia Felix (1907), which overlooks the Magellan Strait. If the desired granite was not obtainable in the area, however, it was sometimes quarried elsewhere and then transported to the construction site. This occurred in British-ruled Canada, when shiploads of granite traveled 16,000 miles (260,000 kilometers) from Scotland to British Columbia to be incorporated into such Imperial Towers as that on Fisgard Island (1860).

Although durable masonry towers began to be built in quantity during the eighteenth century, during the nineteenth century they became the standard form of onshore lighthouse for making lights in most countries. Once the most effective design template had been established, they were rapidly built and, on most sites, relatively inexpensive. Since speed of construction and cost-efficiency were important to the world's lighthouse administrations, brick also became a popular construction material during the second half of the nineteenth century. Manufactured cheaply, brick also offered an efficient alternative material in areas where stone was difficult to quarry. Brick was lighter than stone, too, which meant that towers could be raised to greater heights. Although it had been common practice to line the interior of stone lighthouses with brick as an insulating or earthquake-prevention measure (a practice that continued into the twentieth century, as demonstrated by Japan's Izumo-Hinomisaki Lighthouse of 1903), brick now became a primary construction material.

The U.S. Lighthouse Board pursued a vigorous program of upgrading and constructing lighthouses following its creation in 1852, and many of the structures erected under its auspices were of brick. For example, despite the installation of a first-order Fresnel lens (1856) in the original lighthouse of brick-lined wood at Cape Lookout, on Core Banks Island, North Carolina (1812), this was a temporary upgrade: the decision had already been taken to replace the 96-foot (29-meter) tower. The new brick lighthouse, which was completed in 1859 and stood at a height of 150

Above: *Fisgard Lighthouse (1860) at the entrance to Esquimalt Harbor, British Columbia. Although its foundations are granite, the tower and adjacent keepers' quarters are brick.*

Pages 80–81: *Florida's second St. Augustine Lighthouse (1874) is a 161-foot (50.3-meter) tower typical of many of the beacons along the United States' southern Atlantic coastline.*

A Cylindrical Stone Tower

Hook Head, County Wexford, Ireland

As well as being the oldest of Ireland's eighty-plus lighthouses, Hook Head Light bears the distinction of being one of the world's most ancient aids to navigation still to perform its life-saving function. The waters around the headland are known as the "Graveyard of a Thousand Ships," because of the combination of dangerous winds, currents and isolated rocks. Initiated by the Anglo-Norman nobleman Raymond le Gros, the construction of the formidable stone tower was completed in 1172, rising to a height of 114.8 feet (35 meters) above Waterford Harbour, on Ireland's southeastern coast. The lantern room, however, was not erected until 1791, the passage of six centuries accounting for the tower and lantern's discrepancies in width and architectural style. Indeed, it would have proven unnecessarily difficult to have built the lantern room to equal the tower's impressive diameter of 39.4 feet (12 meters), with walls 9 to 13 feet (3 to 4 meters) thick. Today's optics, which were electrified in 1972 and automated in 1996, were installed in 1911, and continue to exhibit a flashing white character.

1 *The lantern's rotation mechanism.*
2 *The lantern room was a later addition to the light tower.*
3 *Stone steps built into the old light-tower walls.*

4 *A cast-iron staircase leads to the lantern room.*
5 *A slitlike window.*
6 *One of the tower's two original twelfth-century fireplaces.*

A Conical Masonry Tower

Old Head of Kinsale, County Cork, Ireland

The picturesque fishing port of Kinsale, on the River Bandon Estuary, is the site of an old Celtic settlement, and was an infamous piracy center in the fifteenth century. It is, however, perhaps best known for the sinking of the liner *Lusitania*, which was torpedoed off the Old Head of Kinsale in 1915, a tragedy that the keepers of the nearby lighthouse were powerless to prevent. In 1853 this 98-foot (30-meter) conical masonry tower assumed the function of its 1814 predecessor, whose high elevation had caused its light frequently to be obscured by fog. (The first lighthouse on the Head of Kinsale dated from the 1650s.) In common with many contemporary light towers of this type, the masonry—an inexpensive, yet durable, material—that was used in its construction has proved equal to the wild weather conditions that routinely assault it. Under the auspices of the Commissioners of Irish Lights, the light was automated in 1987 and today continues to provide an invaluable service to mariners approaching this dramatically indented coastline. Painted black with two white bands, the lighthouse has a 792,000-candela flashing optic, electric horn fog signals and a radio beacon.

1 *The unobstructed view of the surrounding coastline from the gallery.*

2 *The meticulously maintained electrified first-order optic.*

3 *Detail of the tower's main staircase and central column.*

4 *One of three cranks controlling access to the virtually frictionless mercury bath that enables the lens to rotate.*

5 *The tower's window openings reveal the thickness of the structure's stone walls.*

Left: *The brick structure of* El Faro Viejo *("the Old Lighthouse"), in Mexico's Baja California, now abandoned.*

Opposite: *Race Rocks Light was the second lighthouse to go into operation in British Columbia, in 1860. Its granite blocks were quarried in Scotland and shipped 16,000 sea miles to Victoria.*

Below: *The light station near Prerow, in Mecklenburg-West Pomerania, Germany.*

feet (47 meters), was one of the first U.S. conical "tall towers," which ranged along the Atlantic coast from New York's Fire Island Light (1858), standing 167 feet (50.9 meters) tall, to Florida's Dry Tortugas Light at Loggerhead Key (1858), 157 feet (48 meters) in height. Other notable tall towers built to replace lighthouses whose performance or structure had proved less than satisfactory was the nation's tallest—North Carolina's Cape Hatteras Lighthouse of 1870, which soars to a height of 193 feet (59 meters) from a foundation of iron piles topped with a timber grillage and granite.

It was not only in the United States that brick became a lighthouse-industry standard material, for brick light towers can be seen all over the world. Germany's conical Staberhuk Lighthouse (1903), on Fehmarn Island on the Baltic Sea, is of brick construction, as is Poland's octagonal Niechorze Lighthouse of 1866, another Baltic sentinel. The oldest brick lighthouse in Japan is the Inubo-Saki on Cape Inubo, which rises 102 feet (31 meters) above the Pacific Ocean and was completed in 1874 (until that date, Japanese brick making had not reached the standard necessary to guarantee the survival of such a tall structure).

A Tapered Brick Tower

Fire Island Light, New York

Some of the stones reclaimed from its 1826 predecessor were used to build the foundations of this typical elegantly tapered brick lighthouse, which was lit for the first time on November 1, 1858. It is a measure of the importance of the black-and-white-banded Fire Island Light—which is situated on a barrier island off the southern shore of Long Island near New York Harbor—that the 167-foot (50.9-meter) tower was equipped with a first-order Fresnel lens, among the first in U.S. lighthouse history. When detailing the inadequacies of the site's first light, the Lighthouse Board specified both a higher elevation (which could be more readily achieved with bricks than with heavier stone) and "the most powerful lens apparatus that can be found" for the new beacon. Its flashing white signal, which can be seen 25 miles (40 kilometers) out to sea, caused it to be dubbed the "Winking Woman." The lighthouse was decommissioned in 1973 and now serves as a maritime museum.

1 *The powerful modern optic has a range of 25 miles (40 kilometers).*

2 *The winding staircase spirals upward, supported by a central column.*

3 *The gallery and lantern room.*

4 *Windows on two levels light the tower's stairwell.*

5 *A covered walkway connects the light tower and keeper's quarters.*

Cross-Section of a Conical Lighthouse

Gatun Lighthouse, Panama

Typically between 100 and 150 feet (30 to 45 meters) in height, tall light towers usually conformed to a standard template, the result of the engineering constraints imposed by the necessity to minimize wind resistance and to raise the light to as high an elevation as possible. Being inexpensive, rapidly manufactured and relatively light, brick was the preferred building material in the nineteenth century; the successive courses could be mortared into place relatively easily. Other materials, including stone and cast iron, were also commonly used to construct lighthouses of this type

Rising skyward from a rubblestone foundation, the tower usually assumed a tapered or conical shape for minimal resistance to winds. The lantern room at the summit was reached by means of stairs that were either built into the walls or wended their way upward around a supporting central column. An exterior gallery encircled the lantern room, providing access to the window's exterior surfaces for cleaning and maintenance. Storage areas and, where no adjacent dwelling could be built, the keeper's quarters, occupied the cramped interior spaces of the tower.

The light tower pictured at left is Gatun Lighthouse, located in the Panama Canal. Completed in 1914, the Panama Canal is 51.2 miles (80 kilometers) long, connects the Atlantic and Pacific Oceans and is considered an engineering marvel. The Gatun Locks are one of three sets of locks that allow vessels to navigate the canal.

CAST-IRON TOWERS

The improvements in industrial processes and techniques attendant upon the Industrial Revolution enabled nineteenth-century lighthouse builders to take advantage of a newly developed material: cast iron. Light, malleable, water-resistant and hard-wearing, as well as cheap to produce, cast iron had a number of advantages over masonry. One of its drawbacks, however, was that because cast-iron lighthouses were lighter in weight, they could not withstand the turbulent weather conditions that prevailed at more exposed sites as well as their masonry counterparts. As a precautionary measure, many cast-iron towers, including the second Nobska Point Lighthouse at the harbor of Woods Hole, Massachusetts (1876), were given extra stability by means of a brick lining, which also provided insulation. The effectiveness of reinforcing and stabilizing cast-iron lighthouses in such a way was dramatically demonstrated during the record-breaking hurricane that hit Galveston, Texas, in 1900. The brick-lined cast-iron lighthouse at Bolivar Point (1873) not only stood firm against the onslaught of wind and water, but also provided refuge for 125 of Galveston's citizens. It served the same purpose for fifty more storm-bound people who found shelter there during another hurricane in 1915. Nevertheless, cast-iron towers were deemed better suited to relatively sheltered harbor and headland locations, such as Portsmouth Harbor, New Castle Island, in New Hampshire, which received a cast-iron lighthouse in 1877.

To produce cast iron, iron ore was first smelted with coke in a blast furnace to extract the iron from the ore. The resultant soft metal was then alloyed when molten with a carbon-containing metal to form a harder iron variant, which was then cast into the requisite shape by pouring it into prepared molds. For lighthouses, these generally took

Right: *The cast-iron Nauset Beach Light was one of a pair that stood at Chatham from 1877 until its removal to North Eastham, Massachusetts, in 1923.*

Previous page: *Kommetje Lighthouse is a typical example of a cast-iron beacon whose components were manufactured off-site before being assembled at its eventual location, in this case near Cape Town, South Africa.*

Opposite: *The steel components of New York's Tarrytown Lighthouse were assembled above a pier on the Hudson River in 1883.*

the shape of curved or rectangular plates, or cone segments, with flanges (rims) round the edges. Once the required number of plates was cast, they were numbered for constructional purposes and transported to the lighthouse site, where they were assembled in numerical order by bolting the flanges together above foundations that were similar to those used for masonry structures.

The prefabricated cast-iron lighthouse, which was usually conical in form, proved a boon for such remote, unindustrialized areas as New Zealand, whose oldest light tower, the Pencarrow Head Lighthouse, on South Island, was erected in 1859 from cast-iron plates shipped in from England. Should encroaching erosion threaten the lighthouse site, the tower's cast-iron components could be unbolted and reassembled at a safer location, a strategy that was carried out successfully in 1893–94, when Florida's second Cape Canaveral Lighthouse (1868) was rebuilt in a less vulnerable position, and in 1885, when South Carolina's second Hunting Island Lighthouse (1875) was also moved inland.

Another advantage of cast-iron plates was that they offered a speedy and simple way to

Right: *Canada's Ferryland Lighthouse was raised in 1871. Cast-iron lighthouses were especially favored in its home province of Newfoundland.*

A Brick-Lined Cast-Iron Tower

Stratford Point Light, Connecticut

Stratford Point, at the mouth of the Housatonic River on the Long Island Sound, has witnessed numerous experiments with lighting apparatus since a low, wooden light tower was first erected at this site in 1821, the original lamp giving way to Winslow Lewis's lamp-and-reflector system, which were superseded by a fifth-order Fresnel lens, followed by a pair of range lenses and subsequently a third-order Fresnel lens. Eventually, however, it was deemed necessary to replace the original lighthouse with a durable cast-iron tower, whose prefabricated components were assembled in 1881. The second Stratford Lighthouse was lined with brick to endow its lightweight superstructure with additional stability and insulation. It received a fourth-order Fresnel lens in 1933, and its effectiveness as a daymark was increased by white and red-brown paintwork. Now automated, the lighthouse beams out its light at a focal-plane height of 52 feet (15.8 meters) above sea level.

1 *The optic and the view from the lantern room over Long Island Sound.*

2 *A tiny, porthole-type window near the stairs leading to the lantern room.*

3 *A rotating vent controls air exchange.*

4 *The winding main staircase and the center-level window of the brick-lined tower.*

***Right:** Since its completion in 1873, the brick-lined cast-iron lighthouse at Bolivar Point, near Galveston, Texas, has withstood devastating hurricanes, providing shelter during the worst of these for beleaguered local residents.*

***Page 96:** When it was first raised on its concrete foundations in 1899, the lantern room of Wisconsin's Sturgeon Bay Ship Canal Light was supported solely by a central cylinder and latticed buttresses. Having been stressed by high winds, however, in 1903 it was necessary to replace the structure with the existing steel skeleton tower.*

***Page 97:** The Cape San Blas Light, near Port St. Joe, on Florida's Gulf of Mexico coast, has had a dramatic history, with three lighthouses having successively succumbed to the force of hurricanes, war and erosion. Among the many advantages of the present skeleton tower, which was erected in 1885, is that it can easily be moved if erosion threatens, as occurred in 1919.*

protect or reinforce a storm-battered masonry structure. One example of a lighthouse that benefited from this treatment is Big Sable Point, at Ludington, on Lake Michigan's eastern shore. This 107-foot (33-meter) conical brick tower, built in 1867, had suffered so badly from severe weather conditions that during the twentieth century it had to be enshrouded with cement and have iron plates riveted to the exterior.

Britain pioneered cast-iron lighthouses, and the first is believed to have been built at Swansea, Wales, in 1803. And it was a British engineer, Alexander Gordon, who erected the first cast-iron lighthouse in the New World, at Morant Point, Jamaica (1840), using plates manufactured in England. He reprised this successful formula at Gibbs Hill, in Bermuda, in 1846. Recognizing the practical benefits of cast iron, builders around the world soon emulated Britain's example. Among the late nineteenth- and early twentieth-century cast-iron lighthouses that still display their lights are those on Amédée Island, French New Caledonia (which took only nine months to construct after the parts had arrived from France in 1865); at Pellworm, Germany (1907); and the Færder Lighthouse, on Lille Færder Island, at the entrance to Norway's Oslo Fjord (1857). Given Britain's seminal role in the development of these structures, it is perhaps ironic that only one survives in the British Isles: the light at Whitford Point, in South Wales. Erected in 1865 in place of a wooden lighthouse of 1854, this 130-foot (40-meter) tower was deactivated in 1926. Now classified and protected as an "ancient monument," the Whitford Point structure was being offered for sale for a mere £1.00 (approximately $1.50), as reported on February 16, 2000, by the London newspaper *The Times*. The token price reflected the estimated £100,000 (approximately $150,000) required to restore it.

SKELETON TOWERS

The skeleton lighthouses that were introduced during the second half of the nineteenth century were a variation on the cast-iron-tower theme. Indeed, early skeleton light towers were made of cast iron until the harder iron alloy, steel, overtook it as the lighthouse builder's preferred material. There is a fundamental difference between these iron lighthouse types, however, for, as their name suggests, the superstructure of skeleton lighthouses consists essentially of bare constructional "bones"; without "flesh," or structural infill, the towers present less resistance to wind and waves than their solid counterparts and are likelier to survive such extreme weather conditions as hurricanes and tidal waves. Because they are also lighter than masonry and cast-iron towers, they are also more suitable for soft sandy or muddy locations where only light pile foundations can be used, making them popular choices as beach or range lights. In the United States, this type of lighthouse replaced many along the East Coast that had suffered environmental damage, and a number of such skeleton towers still function. They include the light at Cape Charles, on Virginia's Smith Island, erected in 1895 to replace a brick tower from 1864 that became threatened by coastal erosion. On Chandeleur Island, Louisiana, a skeleton tower built in 1896 assumed the function of its predecessor, a brick tower of 1856 whose foundations had been fatally undermined by hurricane-driven waves. However, others no longer stand, although their demise has generally been due to administrative decisions rather than to intrinsic problems with their construction. One such is Virginia's Hog Island Light, which served from 1896 until it was demolished in 1948. (It was here that a disturbing incident reminiscent of Alfred Hitchcock's famous movie *The Birds* (1963) occurred in 1900, when flocks of birds repeatedly attacked the lantern and its keepers.)

The lighthouse at Cape Charles was constructed according to what soon became the standard template for skeleton towers: a central cylinder—9 feet (3 meters) wide at Cape Charles—housing a spiral stairway to the lantern, which soared upward (in this case to a height of 191 feet, or 58 meters) with four, and sometimes eight, supporting columns. These were strengthened by a bracing network of horizontal and diagonal crossbars, tapering downward in pyramidal form from the apex of the central cylinder to the ground, into which the structure was secured with iron piles. Although the Lingao (Lamko Ih) Lighthouse, on China's Hainan Island, which first displayed its light in 1894, conforms to this type, variations can be seen in Estonia, whose Ruhnu Lighthouse (1877) is devoid of crossbars, and in Japan, whose Hime-Saki Lighthouse (1895) consists of cast-iron plates, with only the central section of skeleton construction.

As with cast-iron structures, the sectional components of skeleton towers, which were manufactured in a range of heights, typically 10, 20, 30, or 40 feet (3, 6, 9, or 12 meters), could be prefabricated in the manufactory ready for assembly at the lighthouse site. The 132-foot (40-meter) Hillsboro Inlet Light, for example, was manufactured in Chicago and shipped down the Mississippi River to be exhibited at the St. Louis Exposition of 1904 before being reassembled on Pompano Beach, Florida, in 1907. In addition, the ease with which the skeleton structure could be disassembled and reassembled offered several options. The tower could be heightened later by slotting in additional sections at the base, or the entire structure could be relocated. For instance, the components of the skeleton tower at Schooner Ledge, Maine, which was erected in 1869, were transported to, and then reassembled at, the light's current site on Michigan Island, one of the Apostle Islands in Lake Superior, Wisconsin, in 1930.

Left: *Demonstrating the versatility of the skeleton construction, some components of the 111-foot (33.8-meter) tower that was erected in 1894 at Rawley Point, Two Rivers, Wisconsin, on the western shore of Lake Michigan, once formed part of a beacon at the mouth of the Chicago River.*

Right: *The Duluth Harbor South Breakwater Inner Lighthouse, Minnesota, is a 67-foot (20.4-meter) skeleton tower that was built in 1901 to act as one of a pair of range lights illuminating the waters of Duluth Inner Harbor.*

Below: *The skeleton tower at Hillsboro Inlet Light was exhibited at the St. Louis Exposition of 1904 before going into active service at Florida's Hillsboro Beach, near Fort Lauderdale, in 1907.*

Exotic Forms and Flourishes

Since classical antiquity, certain lighthouses have taken striking and unusual forms that seize the imagination and contribute to the aura of legend and mystery surrounding these prominent towers, from the gigantic Colossus of Rhodes to New York's landmark Statue of Liberty.

The Colossus of Rhodes was numbered among the Seven Wonders of the World. Supported by a pair of monumental stepped pedestals, this bronze statue of the Sun god Helios stood more than 100 feet (30 meters) high, and the fires lighted within it shone out through its eyes and the brazier in its upraised hand. Designed by Chares of Lindos, it took twelve years to build (to c. 290 BC) and survived only eighty years before it was felled by an earthquake.

From the time of Charlemagne, in AD 800, French mariners feared the rocks and islands at the mouth of the River Gironde, where it flows into the Bay of Biscay. The island of Cordouan was especially dangerous, and in 1584 King Henri III commissioned the renowned architect Louis de Foix to build a lighthouse here. The incredibly elaborate structure—twenty-seven years in the building—comprised a circular stone base 135 feet (41 meters) in diameter that supported a multilevel stone tower with ornamental columns, balustrades, hooded windows, gables, cornices and finials. The tower soared to a height of 221 feet (67.5 meters) and was entered through a grand hall—the royal chamber—surmounted by a richly appointed chapel with a vaulted ceiling. High above was the lantern, where the fire burned in a wire basket. Subsequent alterations have increased the efficiency of the illumination here, but fortunately, de Foix's lower section has been preserved.

Another memorable tower resulted from Henry Winstanley's pioneering efforts to light the notorious Eddystone Rocks, 14 miles (23 kilometers) off the port of Plymouth, England. The British government commissioned him to construct a lighthouse on the reef that had claimed so many ships in 1696. Built of wood, the tower clung precariously to an exposed portion of the reef. Winches, storm-warning signal arms and weathervanes protruded here and there to gauge the wind's direction and hoist supplies, including the sixty great tallow candles that burned in the lantern. First lighted in 1698, the original tower, some 50 feet (15 meters) tall, was severely weakened by the surf and winter storms: waves surged so high that their spray extinguished the light. In 1699 Winstanley and his crew built the tower 40 feet (12 meters) higher and relit it. Their perseverance gave Eddystone's first light a three-year lease of life, but in 1703, while Winstanley and his men were making repairs, a great storm swept the tower away and drowned the work party.

In the Far East, China's paired Jingxin Pagodas, on an island in the Ou River at Wenzhou, have reportedly been used as seamarks for more than a thousand years. The port is some 19 miles (30 kilometers) from the river's outlet into the China Sea, and the estuary is obstructed by many small islands, including the site of the Jingxin Pagodas, East and West, built in 869 and 969 respectively. The multitiered East Pagoda is aligned with the taller polygonal West Pagoda so that they serve as lights in line for mariners coming into port through the channel that they mark. Embowered by trees, the ancient brick-and-stone towers command opposite ends of the island, appearing to float above the small graceful houses that dot the shoreline.

One of the best-known European lighthouses of recent times is Germany's beautiful Bremerhaven Light (1854), built in the Gothic Revival style by Simon Loschen, the same architect who designed the historic port's principal church. Their visual affinity is seen in their red-brick towers, pointed windows, decorative pilasters and multilevel gables and balustrades. The 121-foot (37-meter) tower supports a polygonal glass-and-iron lantern with a crownlike roof surmounted by a weathervane. A dozen different lighthouses now guard Bremerhaven's waterways, but this, the city's first beacon, with its decorative wrought-iron arm once used to hoist storm-warning signals, is the dowager queen of the River Weser.

—Robin Langley Sommer,
Architectural Historian

REINFORCED-CONCRETE TOWERS, ALUMINUM AND FIBERGLASS

Just as the evolution of manufacturing processes had resulted in the building of brick, cast-iron and then steel lighthouses during the course of the nineteenth century, so the twentieth century was the harbinger of both new materials and construction techniques for onshore lighthouses. The first innovation was the introduction of concrete reinforced with steel, a combination that resulted in extraordinary hardness, and thus durability, on the one hand, and great tensile strength on the other. Although concrete had previously been used in lighthouse construction—for example, for the Gandiole Lighthouse in Senegal, West Africa, which was completed in 1836, the refinement of reinforcing concrete with steel was not introduced for another one-and-a-half centuries. In order to make reinforced concrete, a mixture of cement, gravel, sand and water is poured into a mold containing steel rods and is then allowed to dry out until it has set. Prestressed concrete is manufactured according to the same principle, except that steel piano wires, rather than rods, are used. Not only is it simple to produce, reinforced concrete costs less and requires far less maintenance than iron, both important considerations for lighthouse authorities.

The main benefit of embedding steel in concrete is that because steel is ductile, it can withstand enormous levels of tensile or shear stress (deformation as a result of excess torsion, or twisting) without fracturing. Thus reinforced concrete is ideal for sites that are threatened by seismic activity, which is why they are especially common in areas that are prone to earthquakes, like the U.S. West Coast and the shores of Japan. In the case of Japan, however, rather than rebuilding existing lighthouses from scratch, during the 1980s and '90s many brick or stone structures were given additional tensile strength by reinforcing them with steel bars, carbon fiber and prestressed concrete. Such precautionary measures were taken at the stone light

Below: *Minnesota's Split Rock Light has loomed commandingly on a sheer clifftop above Lake Superior since its construction in 1910. Its octagonal brick and reinforced concrete tower was constructed around a framework of steel girders to give it extra stability.*

tower on Mikomoto-Shima Island (which was constructed by the British engineer R.H. Brunton in 1870) and at the Inubo-Saki brick lighthouse at Cape Inubo (another Brunton tower), dating from 1874.

The first U.S. reinforced-concrete lighthouse replaced a brick tower that had stood at Point Arena, California, from 1870 until 1906, when it was irreparably damaged by the earthquake that wreaked such devastation upon San Francisco. At a height of 115 feet (35 meters), this cylindrical reinforced-concrete tower has served unscathed since 1908, despite its vulnerable position directly above the San Andreas fault line. A program of erecting reinforced-concrete light towers rapidly followed, starting with the construction of the second lighthouse on California's Alcatraz Island in 1909 (the first, a Cape Cod-style structure, completed in 1854, was demolished after the 1906 earthquake in preparation for building the island's notorious maximum-security prison). This octagonal, 84-foot (26-meter) tower still houses a functioning light. Similar beacons were built in two other U.S. states plagued by seismic activity: Hawaii and Alaska. Among Hawaii's reinforced-concrete lighthouses are those on Molokai Island (1909), at Kilauea Point, Kauai (1913), and on Diamond Head, Oahu (1918). Reinforced-concrete construction in Alaska, which usually took the form of integrated light towers and dwellings, began in 1923 with the beacon at Point Retreat and continued with notable lights including Cape Spencer (1925) and Cape Hinchinbrook (1934). One of the most recent American lighthouses of this type is that on Oak Island, North Carolina (1958), a silo-style structure, which was constructed from the bottom up by means of the slip-form method. It stands 155 feet (47 meters) tall.

The reinforced-concrete construction formula has been successfully applied to many of the world's lighthouses, including that at Canada's Estevan Point, on Vancouver Island. It was completed in 1909 under the supervision of Colonel William P. Anderson, an innovative engineer who gave the 100-foot (30.5-meter) light tower the additional support of reinforced-concrete flying buttresses. Another Canadian lighthouse that shares Estevan Point's rocketlike shape and flying buttresses is the second tower at Point Atkinson, located at the entrance to Burrard Bay, Vancouver; the hexagonal structure was built in 1912. The Cotonou Lighthouse in Benin, West Africa, which first displayed its light in 1928, demonstrates a harmonious combination of reinforced concrete and steel, in which a square, open-lattice steel tower rises from a reinforced-concrete dwelling-type foundation. Indeed, despite the introduction of new high-tech materials into the annals of lighthouse construction later in the twentieth century, reinforced concrete and steel continued to play an important role in the lighthouse builder's repertoire.

Above: *The futuristic-looking Escuminac Point Light, New Brunswick.*

Below: *Twentieth-century lighthouses, such as this sleek example in the harbor of Cannes, southern France, combine traditional components with durable, economical materials and advanced construction methods.*

Both aluminum and fiberglass made their debut into the field of lighthouse construction during the second half of the twentieth century. The element aluminum is contained within bauxite ore, from which it is extracted by electrolysis before being alloyed with another metal and then anodized, or coated with a protective film of oxide, also by electrolysis. The resultant aluminum alloy is strong, highly malleable, more resistant to corrosion than iron or steel, and extremely light—hence its use in aircraft components. Fiberglass, which is similarly durable and light, is created either by spinning molten glass through holes bored into a rotating dish, or by pulling the glass through spinnerets (finely perforated dispensers), after which the fine matted fibers of spun glass are bonded with synthetic resin or plastic to form a substance ideal for use in the bodies of automobiles, boats and aircraft, as well as monopoles (single-column poles).

Although the use of aluminum in lighthouses was initially restricted to the lantern, it was gradually extended to encompass the tower itself. The first U.S. lighthouse to make use of this new industrial material was the reinforced-concrete tower at New Charleston, on the northern shore of the entrance to South Carolina's Charleston Harbor. It was constructed in 1962 to replace the second lighthouse (1876) on Morris Island, a masonry tower whose future was menaced by the erosion that eventually claimed the island (though not the lighthouse). New Charleston is the only U.S. lighthouse whose lantern is reached by means of an elevator rather than a stairway. Its unusual triangular shape, along with its aluminum-panel cladding and its light (originally 28 million candelas, since reduced to 1.2 million), which was once the Western Hemisphere's most powerful, combined to make this 163-foot (49.7-meter) tower a highly innovative structure. (Paradoxically, however, despite its many novel features, this was also the last American lighthouse to conform to the traditional blueprint.) Aluminum is now used both as cladding for lighthouses and for upgrading the lanterns. Canada's Sambro Island stone lighthouse, which has stood since 1759, received an aluminum lantern in 1968, after its old iron lantern (1906) was dismantled.

It was Britain's lighthouse-administration service, Trinity House, to which credit (or curses, depending on your viewpoint) must go for first recognizing the primary advantage that fiberglass offered lighthouse authorities: ease of maintenance and a concomitant reduction in cost. Fiberglass is usually used for construction of the monopoles that support today's lightweight plastic lenses and aerobeacons. The process of replacing traditional towers with lights set on monopoles had already started before fiberglass arrived on the scene, early poles being made of metal. For example, the light that was beamed out from the Cape Cod-style lighthouse on Raspberry Island, one of Wisconsin's Apostle Islands, was rendered obsolete in 1957 by a solar-powered 160-candela light that was set atop a metal monopole nearer the edge of the bluff on which the lighthouse had been constructed in 1863. The lighthouse itself, today a much-visited museum piece, still stands, however, as does Hawaii's Kilauea Point Light (1913), whose aerobeacon has been supported by a monopole since 1976. Although such lights may need inspecting only once each year, those who are moved by the romance inherent in the traditional lighthouse are less appreciative of such cost-cutting measures, particularly when a "soulless" plastic light on a fiberglass pole creates the very real danger that an historic lighthouse may be demolished.

Above: *The reinforced-concrete tower of Canada's early twentieth-century Pointe-au-Père Lighthouse, on the St. Lawrence River, was designed by Colonel William P. Anderson to incorporate supportive flying buttresses.*

WAVE-SWEPT BEACONS

The Technology of Offshore, Reef and Breakwater Lighthouses

***Previous pages:** Sturgeon Bay Ship Canal North Pierhead Lighthouse, Wisconsin, pictured in silhouette at the end of the long walkway-topped pier that juts into the bay. Completed in 1882, it is one of the more elaborate pierhead lights on the Great Lakes.*

The challenge of constructing lighthouses at difficult offshore, reef and breakwater sites required remarkable feats of engineering. With a few notable exceptions, before the mid-nineteenth century no one had the knowledge, experience, or technology to build permanent aids to navigation at certain notorious offshore troublespots that had claimed countless mariners' lives. Shoals and reefs, for example, were dreaded by sailors, because their treacherous rocks, corals, or sandbanks were often submerged: only when a vessel ran aground did their danger become tragically apparent. Such a reef was Skerryvore, off Scotland's Atlantic coast, which Robert Stevenson, the pioneering lighthouse builder and constructor of the Bell Rock Lighthouse, described in 1834 as the "terror of the Mariner." Illustrating the need for a lighthouse on the Skerryvore reef, its eventual builder, Robert's son, Alan, wrote of one vessel's lucky escape through the intervention of his surveyors: "A large vessel belonging to Yarmouth, with a cargo of timber, was actually boarded...by the surveyors, who warned the Master of his danger in having nearly approached these rocks, of the existence of which his chart gave no indication."

Although some lighthouse authorities attempted to warn mariners of such dangerous hazards by positioning lightships nearby, these ships were as vulnerable to storm winds and waves as any other vessel, making it clear that a stable permanent installation was needed. However, this option could not be implemented until an effective method of rooting the lighthouse to the shoal had been devised—a conundrum that exercised the imagination and energy of the nineteenth-century builders to their limits. Not only was it necessary to find a means of securing a heavy structure to unyielding bedrock, but the fact that many such sites were accessible only by boat in good weather and at low tide created a logistical headache.

River estuaries like the Mississippi Delta and sandy coastlines presented a different problem: how to erect a lighthouse on muddy or sandy foundations in such a way that its weight could be supported to prevent it from sinking into the soft substratum or shifting and breaking up. This apparently insurmountable difficulty deterred many prospective lighthouse builders

***Below:** Constructed in 1905, Boston, Massachusetts', Graves Ledge Light, went into operation nearly two hundred years after its neighbor on Little Brewster Island, the intervening centuries having seen pioneering advances in building technology for offshore beacons. The granite tower is 113 feet (34.4 meters) tall.*

over the centuries, yet because many such rivers and stretches of coastline led to busy ports and harbors, a nation's commercial prosperity demanded the construction of permanent aids to navigation at these locations. In cases where breakwaters were deemed necessary, either to ward against coastal erosion or to protect ships approaching harbor from destructive winds and waves, lighthouses were also required, both to guide vessels safely to their docking places and to warn mariners of the presence of the breakwater itself, which would be obscured from view in dark and foggy conditions and could present another very real hazard. Yet inherent in the construction of breakwater or pier lighthouses was an additional set of challenges, not least the frustrated fury of the winds and waves as they assaulted the exposed breakwater with their full force.

Prior to the advent of the Industrial Revolution, which contributed a new array of materials and engineering techniques to the lighthouse builders' armory, overcoming the obstacles to building wave-swept towers seemed an optimistic pipe dream. Even so, a handful of determined people rose to the challenge, sometimes paying for their failures with their lives. The few who succeeded, however, not only changed the course of lighthouse construction, but also inspired others by their example. John Smeaton, who entered the annals of lighthouse lore with the third Eddystone Rock Lighthouse (1759), was among the first to make a fundamental contribution to the constructional principles of offshore lighthouses. Although both Henry Winstanley and John Rudyerd had raised light towers on Eddystone by bolting them to the rock, neither structure proved capable of survival, Winstanley's being swept away by storm waves and Rudyerd's set alight by a lantern fire. Smeaton's tower, however, stood from 1759 until 1882, mainly because the strength and flexibility of its snugly interlocking dovetailed-granite construction, along with its flared foundation and conical shape, enabled it to withstand potential wind and wave damage. Despite its eventual dismantling due to erosion of the rock that supported it, Smeaton's lighthouse was a triumph of engineering and assumed an iconic status. It provided a template for wave-swept lighthouses that was followed by his successors, including Robert and Alan Stevenson, who made modifications as necessary, and revolutionized lighthouse design with the pioneering use of precut, dovetailed granite. Smeaton also made the useful discovery that the most effective form of hydraulic mortar for underwater construction consisted of clay-rich limestone, which hardened into cement despite immersion.

Smeaton's solutions to the difficulties posed by the Eddystone Rock would later be emulated by builders of offshore lighthouses around the world. Yet because each site presented unique challenges, new engineering methods were developed over time to meet them, while industrialization offered increasingly efficient construction materials. This chapter explores the evolution of offshore-lighthouse designs over the centuries after Smeaton's achievement at Eddystone.

Above: *Kyle of Lochalsh Light stands on a wave-swept point on the islet of Eilean Ban, at the entrance to Loch Alsh, midway between the southeastern shores of the Isle of Skye and the western coast of Scotland's Highland region.*

ROCK AND UNDERWATER FOUNDATIONS

The usual methods for constructing foundations for onshore lighthouses were often impracticable for wind- and wave-swept offshore locations where the rock surface is just above or below the sea. However, conventional means served Robert Stevenson in building the Bell Rock Lighthouse (1811), for which a foundation pit 2 feet (60 centimeters) deep, with a diameter of 42 feet (13 meters), was dug into the bedrock of granite in 1807. Since the pit had to be excavated by hand, not only was this laborious and time-consuming work, but it was also impeded by the sea, which constantly rushed in to fill the widening pit. Alan Stevenson adopted a similar approach when digging the foundation pit of the Skerryvore Lighthouse (1844) in 1840, and although his workmen were aided in their arduous task by blasting with dynamite, Stevenson still complained about "the great irregularity of the surface, and the extraordinary hardness and unworkable nature of the material, together with the want of room on the Rock."

Another rock-foundation tower, South Africa's Roman Rock Lighthouse, in False Bay, was raised in 1867 under the supervision of Alexander Gordon and Robert Cousins in a perilous operation that was made even riskier by stormy weather. Roman Rock is exposed only at low tide, which is one reason why the cast-iron plates from which the light was constructed were prepared off site. Gordon and Cousins originally intended to fill the lower 10 feet (3 meters) of the tower with concrete, but when the plates cracked, they were forced to encase the base of the tower in granite walls 4 feet (1.2 meters) thick. One of the best-known U.S. lighthouses on a rock wave-swept foundation was the St. George Reef Light on Northwest Seal Rock, 6 miles (9.5 kilometers) off Point St. George, California. Here George Ballantyne's construction workers dug a foundation pit in the rock before building a huge circular platform of reinforced concrete, with a granite exterior, above it. Although work was hampered by severe storms and the limited working space, the rock being only 300 feet (91 meters)

Below: *The fact that it took six years to construct the Kéréon Light on the Men Tensel reef, off France's Brittany coast, speaks volumes about the difficulties presented by this offshore site. First lit in 1916, the ashlar (hewn-stone) tower, which stands 155 feet (47.25 meters) tall, continues to defy the onslaught of the ocean waves. (© Jean Guichard 1989, AlphaPix)*

Dovetailed Stone Construction

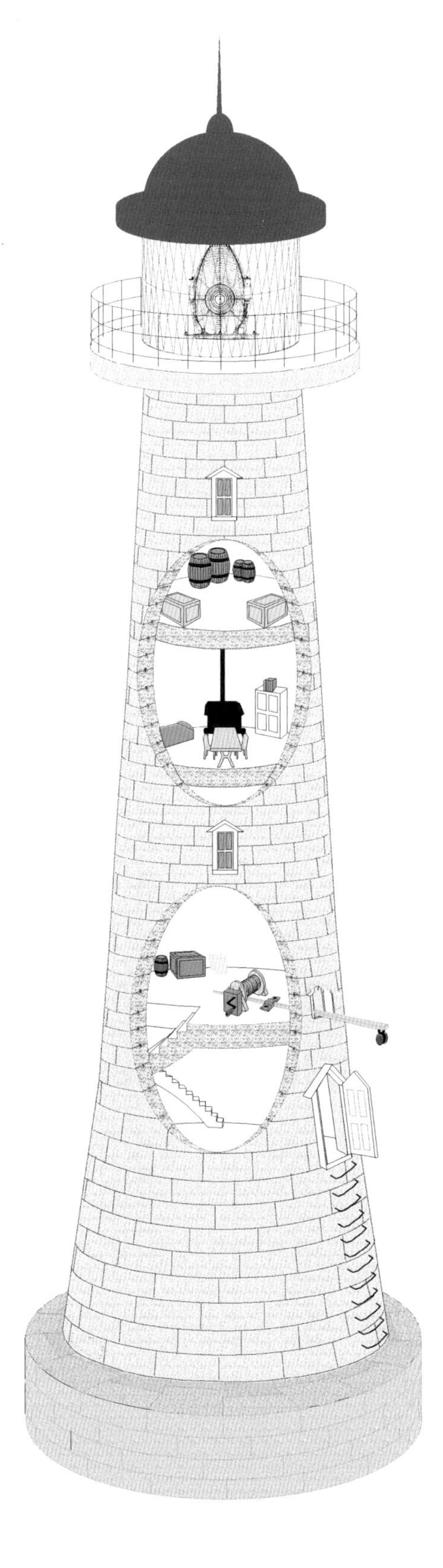

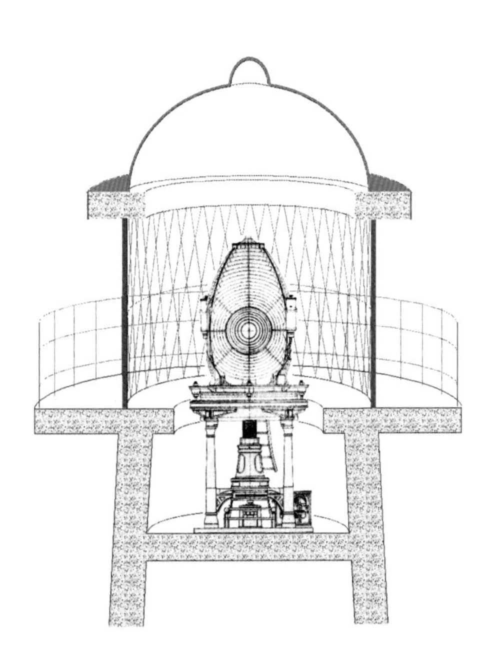

***Above:** Lighter than equivalent single lenses, Fresnel lenses were easily rotated by clockworks housed beneath the arbor supporting the level plane table upon which the Fresnel structure rested.*

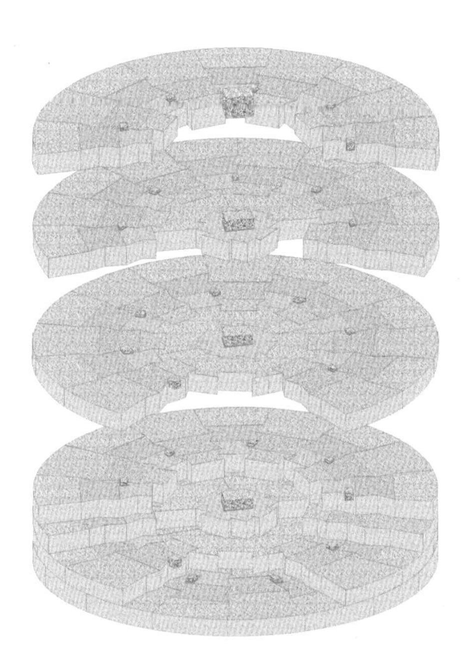

Granite blocks interlocked to hold each other in place were used to form the foundation interface with the native rock upon which the tower was to be built. Adding to the structural integrity of these foundations were marble "dowels" that tightly linked each course of blocks to those above and below it, as seen in the detail below. An early form of prefabrication, the blocks and dowels were cut, fitted and assembled on shore before being moved piecemeal to the construction site.

To improve the ability of many towers to withstand the impact of waves and gale-force winds, loops of steel cable were fitted between courses to better distribute shock forces. These cables were embedded in lead, both to ensure full cohesion between cable and stone and to protect the steel from salt water.

—Glenn O. Myers,
Telecommunications engineer

Right: *Michigan's Rock of Ages Light sits above a reef of basaltic stone in Lake Superior. The 130-foot (40-meter) steel-plated tower was raised above a concrete-filled steel caisson in 1908.*

Below: *France's* La Vieille *("The Old Woman") is anchored to a rock off the coast of Brittany. Construction of lighthouses at perilous offshore sites like this was hindered by high tides and stormy weather. (© Jean Guichard 1989, AlphaPix)*

in diameter, Ballantyne and his crew persevered. The square granite tower that stood upon this manmade platform displayed its light from 1892 until 1975, when the severe local weather conditions made a buoy more appropriate to the site.

Like the St. George Reef Lighthouse, those at Race Rock (1879), New York, and New London Ledge (1909), Connecticut, were built above artificial, concrete-filled granite platforms. Unlike the St. George Reef Light, however, their foundations were constructed on submerged bedrock. With such substantial bases to support them, elaborate multistory lighthouses could be built, with the result that these structures resemble houses marooned on tiny islands. Although both stations remain active, the time, expense and sheer manpower required to raise them prohibited the construction of others: caisson-type foundations provided a much simpler and less expensive alternative.

Above: *The imposing New London Ledge Light, Connecticut, resembles a floating mansion atop its concrete platform.*

Left: *Isolated offshore lighthouses like Norway's Kjeungskjaer Light required sufficient storage room to house months' worth of fuel and supplies.*

STRAIGHTPILE FOUNDATIONS

It was too daunting—and sometimes impossible—to dig foundation pits at some offshore sites, including Smalls Rock, which lies 20 miles (32 kilometers) off Britain's Welsh coast in the Irish Sea. It was on this isolated spot that the world's first viable straightpile-foundation beacon was erected, between 1775 and 1776, under the direction of Henry Whiteside, musical-instrument maker turned lighthouse builder. Because constructing the wooden lighthouse on the rock was unfeasible from scratch, it was built on the mainland, disassembled and transported to its site, where it was reconstructed. During the early phases of the work, Whiteside found the iron piles (posts or columns) that he had originally intended using to be unsatisfactory; he replaced them with oak piles 40 feet (12 meters) long and 24 inches (61 centimeters) in diameter. Nine of these piles were inserted into holes bored in the rock to provide a secure foundation for the octagonal two-story lighthouse. Whiteside's tower stood on Smalls Rock for eighty-five years, and many such lighthouses were subsequently raised on Britain's shores, including those at Mucking (1851), Dovercourt (1863), Thorngumbald (1870) and Bamburgh (1910).

Below: *The second light at Minots Ledge, Cohasset, Massachusetts, which first assumed its duties in 1860, has proved more durable than its pile-foundation predecessor. A conical tower consisting of more than a thousand granite blocks, it tapers to a height of 97 feet (29.5 meters) above sea level. Its designer, General Joseph G. Totten, was influenced by Smeaton's third Eddystone Rock Lighthouse of 1759.*

The first U.S. pile-foundation lighthouse was constructed on Minots Ledge reef, off Cohasset, Massachusetts, under the direction of Captain William Henry Swift. Preparatory work on this difficult site started in 1847 with the drilling of holes 5 feet (1.5 meters) in depth for the nine iron straightpiles. Measuring 10 inches (25.4 centimeters) in diameter and 60 to 63 feet (18 to 19 meters) long, they would support the iron-skeleton tower. This slow process could be undertaken only at low tide and in calm seas. The piles were sunk into the rock to protrude above the water level, one pile in the center and the other eight surrounding it, after which they were secured to the reef with a "cement formed of iron filings." With the piles in place, their upper sections were cross-braced to reinforce them (the lower sections were left open), and a platform was laid across the top of the piles to support the keeper's dwelling and lantern room. Although the lighthouse went into service in 1850, the omission of cross-bracing at the lower levels proved a crucial mistake: in 1851 the structure, and two of its keepers, were swept away by stormy seas, leaving only the truncated piles in place. This unsuccessful pile lighthouse was replaced in 1860 by Captain Barton Stone Alexander: his conical, dovetailed-granite tower, whose base was cemented to the reef, had a more durable foundation. This has enabled the "lovers' light" (a nickname acquired from its flashing sequence, which appears to spell out the words "I l-o-v-e y-o-u") to guide vessels safely through the dangerous Atlantic waters to this day.

Left: The spider-type Love Point Light, Maryland, pictured with its screwpiles besieged by ice in 1902. Screwpile lighthouses failed to survive in ice-prone regions like the Chesapeake Bay.

SCREWPILE LIGHTHOUSES

The vulnerability of the straightpile lighthouse to adverse weather conditions deterred many lighthouse administrations from pursuing this option at locations lashed by storm winds and waves. However, the development and successful use of another form of pile foundation, the screwpile, enabled light towers to be raised at previously untenable offshore sites.

The screwpile tower was the invention of Alexander Mitchell, an Irish engineer working in England, who patented his device during the 1830s. Mitchell hit upon the idea of extending the straightpile by attaching helicoidal (corkscrewlike) flanges, or blades, of iron to one end, reasoning that when the new pile was screwed into the seabed, it would be held securely in place by its spiral flanges. Having translated theory into reality at Maplin Sands, in the estuary of the River Thames, in 1838, he began constructing the first working screwpile lighthouse in the Wyre Estuary, at Fleetwood, off the coast of Lancashire in northwestern England, using iron helicoidal flanges attached to wooden piles. Hailed as a triumph on its lighting in 1840, Mitchell's first-generation screwpile lighthouse inspired builders around the world to emulate, and improve upon, its example.

Screwpile lighthouses were particularly suitable for relatively protected bays, harbors, rivers and sounds with sandy or muddy bases. The first such U.S. lighthouse was built in 1850, at Brandywine Shoal, in Delaware Bay—a two-year operation directed by Major Hartman Bache (whom Mitchell advised). The first lighthouse on Brandywine Shoal had been a straightpile structure that was destroyed in its first year, 1828, when it was flattened by moving ice. To protect his lighthouse from a similar fate, Bache surrounded the structure with an ice-breaker in the form of a circular pier consisting of thirty iron screwpiles reinforced by interconnecting iron rods (a second such "pen" was added in 1857). The eight iron screwpiles that supported the lighthouse itself were screwed into the sand by means of a capstan (a rotating drumlike mechanism) powered by thirty men. The screwpiles were then strengthened by a network of cross-bracing

Below: Screwpile lighthouses conforming to the "spider" design, like New Zealand's Bean Rock Light (1871), which marks the entrance to Waitemata Harbour, just off North Head in Auckland, are particularly suited to relatively sheltered offshore sites. This light was automated in 1912.

and tension rods. The dwelling and lantern room crowned the structure. The U.S. Congress showed its confidence in the new lighthouse's staying power when it authorized installation of one of the nation's first three expensive Fresnel lenses. And, in fact, a light was maintained in its lantern room until 1914, when the lighthouse was replaced with a reinforced-concrete tower after inspection revealed corrosion in the iron screwpiles.

Screwpile lighthouses had much to recommend them, not least their cost. The bill for the Brandywine Shoal Lighthouse, for example, came to a modest $53,317 as compared to a whopping $704,638 for St. George Reef. They were also built quickly (each screwpile took about a day to fix into place), and could be constructed on sites that could support little weight, where only lightships had been considered feasible aids to navigation. These more visible, permanent lights contributed significantly to mariners' safety. Unlike heavy masonry towers, which would either have sunk or teetered dangerously on yielding bases of sand, screwpiles enabled lighthouses to stand firm on soft foundations. Nevertheless, it was necessary to ensure that the supportive piles were not overburdened by heavy lighthouse structures: thus those built in American sounds and bays usually conformed to the "spider" type—low platforms upheld by six to eight spindly legs. As exemplified by Maryland's Thomas Point Shoal Light, located in Chesapeake Bay and completed in 1875, a central iron screwpile was surrounded by another six in a hexagonal pattern, all connected by tension rods and cross-bracing. The platform on top of the screwpiles provided the base for the dwelling-type superstructure, a one-and-one-half-story wooden building surrounded by a gallery, whose lantern room protruded from the center of the roof. Not only were such small towers lightweight, but because they stood in protected waters close to shore, their lights needed a focal plane of only about 50 feet (15 meters). Most of these structures were either hexagonal or octagonal in shape and were constructed of wood. However, Chesapeake Bay's oldest screwpile lighthouse, the Seven Foot Knoll Light—raised in 1855 at the mouth of the Patapsco River, but since moved to Baltimore Harbor—was circular and clad in cast-iron plates, while the screwpile light built in 1871 on Cat Island, off the Mississippi coast, was quadrangular.

There were certain types of offshore sites for which protected screwpile lighthouses were unsuited, particularly those surrounded by deep fast-moving waters. The combination of sand

The first U.S. exposed screwpile lighthouse, which became the blueprint for its successors, was designed by I.W.P. Lewis and constructed under the direction of Lieutenant George G. Meade on Carysfort Reef, northeast of Key Largo, between 1848 and 1852. The lower two-thirds of the lighthouse—eight iron screwpiles anchored 10 feet (3 meters) into the reef and secured with square footplates, above which rose a low circular dwelling—resembled the typical protected screwpile structure in appearance. The crucial variant was the central iron cylinder that rose from the center of the roof to culminate in a lantern, as well as the cross-braced iron pillars arranged in

Left: *The Ship Shoal Light, off Raccoon Point, Louisiana, is a 125-foot (38.1-meter) iron-skeleton tower that was raised in 1859. Its screwpiles are stabilized by iron footplates.*

Below: *Before the 1883 Drum Point Light was retired to the Calvert Maritime Museum, Solomons, Maryland, it stood at the mouth of the Patuxent River. The flanges at the end of the screwpiles measured 3 feet (91 centimeters) in width.*

and uneven surfaces on Florida's soft-foundation coral reefs presented builders with another difficulty: the reef's fundamental instability, which engineers finally countered by driving a straight- or screwpile through an iron disk, or footplate, that rested on the surface of the reef and thereby diffused the weight of the tower over a wider area. Reflecting both this modified screwpile technology and their prevalence on reefs, such exposed screwpile lighthouses are often also classified as reef or diskpile lighthouses. They may also be called tubular skeletal lighthouses, for the form that most of their towers took, which offered less resistance than their solid counterparts to extreme weather. Furthermore, skeletal structures made it possible to raise the light to very high elevations, so that it could be seen from miles away.

The First Screwpile Lighthouse

Wyre Light, Fleetwood, England

"I have been given the gift to see through God's eyes." These were the words of the blind, but brilliant, Irish marine engineer Alexander Mitchell (1780–1868), who invented the screwpile lighthouse, the first lit version of which was built in 1840 at Fleetwood-on-Wyre, off the Fylde Coast in the northwestern English county of Lancashire.

The land on which the port and town of Fleetwood were built was a sterile, rectangular tract of sand dunes and silt, jutting northward between the open Irish Sea and the mouth of the River Wyre, close to the southern end of Morecambe Bay. Some 5 miles (8 kilometers) upstream to the south was the established port of Skippool, where cargoes of flax and tallow were unloaded as long ago as 1590; there was also a shipbuilding yard nearby, at Wardleys, and a Custom House at Poulton-le-Fylde, which served the whole of the Fylde Coast. There was seventeenth-century coastal trade in tobacco, wines, spirits, slate and timber, and during the mid-eighteenth century ships came to Skippool with oranges and sugar from the West Indies and timber from the Baltic. Yet all of this time there was nothing at Fleetwood (not yet even named) except for a deep-water refuge in the mouth of the River Wyre for ships to shelter from the ravages of westerly gales and storms.

Peter Hesketh Fleetwood, the young heir to a fortune of northern English landed estates, influenced by his friendship with the social reformer Robert Owen and the potential for redevelopment opened up by the new railway system, decided to apply his wealth to the creation of a seaport and resort on his land at the mouth of the River Wyre. The nearby ports of Lancaster, Glasson Dock and Preston all had their difficulties with tides and hazardous approaches through shifting sands, and Skippool's trade was restricted by the draft of its traffic up river.

In 1836 Hesketh Fleetwood commissioned a survey of the Lancashire coast by the hydrographer Captain Belcher "to render Wyre Navigation...safer and easier of access." His proposals were published in the *Nautical Magazine* in 1837, but were not adopted. Three years later, Captain Henry Mangly Denham, R.N., issued "Remarks and sailing directions for approaching and navigating the sea reach of the Wyre between North Wharf and Bernard Wharf up to Port Fleetwood with account of lighthouses and Estuary." These proposals were adopted, and included the placing in line of three lighthouses, two of which were on land (part of the new town plan by renowned architect Decimus Burton), and the third was the Wyre Light, 2 miles (3.2 kilometers) out on the northeastern elbow of North Wharf bank at the entrance to the Wyre navigation channel.

The need for the lighthouse was acute in an area where 119 vessels and 122 lives had been lost between 1822 and 1841. Denham's chart showed that the River Wyre flowed in such a way that the sea had a scouring effect on the river bed, so that its natural basin, the Canshe Hole, was preserved. Where the new wharves were constructed, the river narrowed and flowed so fast that all silt deposits were kept in suspension and were carried out to Morecambe Bay, where the crosscurrents of the River Lune swept the silt away and prevented a bar from forming at the Wyre's mouth. This made dredging comparatively simple, and with satisfactory navigational aids for foggy conditions and darkness the way would be opened for Fleetwood to become a night-and-day harbor.

The main difficulty in siting the Wyre Light was that there was no rock, no firm foundation, but only the treacherous and unstable sands of this part of the coast. The answer would be the screwpile foundations patented by Alexander Mitchell in 1833. One day in 1832 Mitchell was experimenting with a sail, which he had directed into the teeth of the wind. He did this by means of a broad-flanged screw in the water and a canvas-covered screw in the air. Mitchell happened to place the water screw on the ground when a sudden gust of wind, propelling the aerial canvas screw violently, embedded the water screw in the ground. Realizing the significance of this, he and his son John planted an experimental screwpile in a sandy bank in Belfast Lough. It remained firmly fixed after a rough night. After building a lighthouse at Maplin Sands, at the entrance to the River Thames, in 1838, the lighthouse at Fleetwood-on-Wyre was planned and executed from his own design by himself and his son in 1839. It was the first screwpile lighthouse in the world to be lighted.

To improve the approach from the Foot of Wyre, the channel between the wharves had been cut and straightened with the help of a 20-horsepower steam dredger. In November 1839 the new screwpile lighthouse was delivered from the Belfast works of Alexander Mitchell and Son aboard the schooner *Collingne*. To erect the frame, a floating raft was built with holes in it to accommodate the piles, which were driven and screwed home by a windlass. The process took nine days. Mitchell had solved the problem of securing foundations to make them immovable in unstable foreshores.

The Wyre Light was lit for the first time in June 1840, the structure having been tested by the severe gales of the preceding winter. To provide for foggy periods, there was a bell that sounded three strokes, with a one-minute pause. In December of that year the two inline lighthouses, which were designed and erected on shore by Decimus Burton, were also illuminated, and thus Port Fleetwood (where there had not been a single building until 1836) was at once truly open to the sea day and night. The lighthouse proved durable. In 1870, for example, the schooner *Elizabeth Jane*, inward bound during dead-calm conditions, failed to hold anchor, drifted into the piles of the Wyre Light, and lifted the keepers' house onto her forecastle, much to the alarm of the two keepers. The vessel was badly damaged, but Mitchell's screwpile structure stood unmoved in the sand bank. In fact, his invention would prove successful in all but ice-prone waters. The Wyre Light (shown at low tide in the archival photograph below), so superior to a wavering lightship, was the focus of worldwide nautical interest. Alexander Mitchell had, through his invention and brilliant execution, provided the means of safe navigation through hazardous waters for thousands of sailors entering harbors with unstable foreshores.

—J. Keith Hunt,
Consultant Architect and Town Planner

Opposite: Thomas Point Shoal Light, Maryland.

midal form around it. The addition of the central cylinder not only raised the light to a height of 106 feet (32 meters), but also contained a stairway by which the keepers could gain access to it. Constructed at a cost of $105,069, the Carysfort Reef Lighthouse is still secure on its square disks, each of which is 4 feet (1.2 meters) wide.

Following the successful precedent at Carysfort Reef, many other exposed screwpile lighthouses were built in Florida waters before and after the Civil War, including Sand Key Light, near Key West. The Lewis-and-Meade partnership completed it in 1853, and it still stands, although the island on which it was built washed away during a hurricane in 1865. Other examples are those at Sombrero Key (1858), Alligator Reef (1873), Fowey Rocks (1878) and American Shoal (1880). Although they were confined primarily to Florida, similar lighthouses were also constructed on Louisiana's Ship Shoal, off Raccoon Point in the Gulf of Mexico, and on Southwest Reef (both 1858). The skeleton lighthouses at Florida's Sombrero Key and Louisiana's Southwest Reef are unusual in that their foot plates were attached to straightpiles rather than screwpiles.

Right: Fowey Rocks Light was constructed off Biscayne Bay in 1878. In common with many of its Florida fellows, the skeleton tower of this reef light presents minimal resistance to storm winds and waves, while footplates stabilize its piles on the soft, uneven sand and coral beneath it.

Mitchell's Pioneering Screwpile Design

Wyre Light, Fleetwood, England

The structure of the Wyre Light was secured to the bank with seven of Mitchell's Patent Screw Piles, each 3 feet (91 centimeters) in diameter. The six outer piles were at the angles of a hexagon, about 46 feet (14 meters) in diameter, and the seventh pile stood vertical at the center. The outer piles were inclined inward, so that the frame connecting the top of the columns, on which the house stood, was contracted to about 27 feet (8.2 meters). Each screwpile was formed of a malleable, iron shaft 15 feet (4.6 meters) long and 5 inches (2 centimeters) in diameter, with a 3-foot (91-centimeter) screw securely fixed to the bottom. At the top end of the iron shaft was a screw for fixing the wooden column to the iron pile. The timber columns were seven logs of Baltic timber, the central one 56 feet (17 meters) long and the outer six 46 feet (14 meters) long. A hole was bored into the lower end of each column to a depth of about 8 feet (2.4 meters). Three iron hoops were driven onto each column at the top, middle and base of the cored length of column for added strength.

Next, each column was raised perpendicularly above the iron pile and screwed by capstan. The foot of the column was then screwed into the sand bank to a depth of about 3 feet (91 centimeters). Once the timber was wet, it expanded and clasped the iron shaft and was bound firmly by the hoops. Hollow, cast-iron capitals were lowered on to the heads of all seven columns. Beams radiated from the central column to the outer six, and the heads of these were secured to each other by further beams.

To give lateral strength to resist a force of about 350 tons, twenty-four angle braces of 1.25-inch (3.2-centimeter) round iron were applied, secured at the top to trusses cast with the capitals and lower down with strong, wrought-iron bands with projecting bolt holes. The braces were keyed up and tensioned at their crossings. The whole structure would prove resistant to stormy seas and colliding vessels.

The superstructure of the lighthouse was conventionally constructed. The central column reached the base of the lantern, and this, together with the strong frame of the keepers' house, added stability to the whole structure, as well as supporting the lantern itself.

The lantern, whose light shone brightly over an 8-mile (12.9-kilometer) horizon, was twelve-sided, with its focal plane about 31 feet (9.4 meters) above the highest spring tide and 44.5 feet (13.6 meters) above the mean high-tide level. The original engineer's drawing of the lighthouse is shown below.

—Keith Hunt,
Consultant Architect and Town Planner

MARKING UNDERWATER HAZARDS: A CASE STUDY

Southern Connecticut's Norwalk, founded in 1649, is a town built primarily on the oystering industry. Its sheltered harbor, protected by several islands, has limited safe access from Long Island Sound because of the obstacles posed by mile-long Greens Ledge, a sandy ledge with isolated rocky protrusions that lies just below the low-tide water level and obstructs much of the mouth of the Norwalk River. The depth soundings shown on the Coast Guard's navigational chart at right illustrate the danger to vessels of running aground unless they circumnavigate its outermost point.

The entrance to the narrow navigable harbor channel was first lighted in 1828 from 53-acre Sheffield Island (formerly Smith Island), a low-lying island on which construction of a light was a relatively simple task. The original crude 30-foot (9-meter) masonry tower, whose remains still lie underwater off the island's shore, was replaced in 1868 by a two-story limestone keeper's dwelling with a short frontal tower (outer fold and inset top center)—one of a series erected along the Sound at that time.

The danger represented by Greens Ledge, however, remained an unsolved problem for mariners entering Norwalk Harbor, especially at night and in poor visibility, as the underwater hazards to safe navigation into the channel were still unmarked. In 1902 recently developed technology—caisson foundations, first used in Germany during the 1880s, and cast-iron prefabrication—enabled construction of a 52-foot (15.6-meter) cylindrical tower on an artificial offshore "island," a caisson anchored directly to the submerged ledge at its outermost point. The new beacon (inset near right) provided optimum guidance into the harbor channel entrance and rendered the Sheffield Island Light obsolete.

Greens Ledge Light remains an active aid to navigation, flashing its alternately red and white light signal at an interval of 4 seconds, as marked on the Coast Guard's navigational chart at right. Automated in 1972, the tower is also fitted with a powerful fog signal. Other aids to navigation around this harbor approach include Peck Ledge Light (inset far right, top) and a series of buoys and markers as shown on the chart.

Aside from marking submerged hazards, offshore foundations have also enabled construction of breakwaters and pierheads, marked with beacons, to improve harbor approaches. Shown on page 123 is Lake Michigan's cast-iron South Haven Light, which is located on a pierhead and accessed by a catwalk. On page 130 is Lyme Point Light, in Old Saybrook, Connecticut, built to mark the end of the breakwater that protects the Connecticut River tidelands.

D11
Q

NORWALK HARBOR
ENTRANCE CHANNEL
NORWALK ISLANDS
COCKENOE
COCKENOE ISLAND
CHIMON I
SHEA I
WHITE POLE
Ram Historical Park
RAM BAY
Calf Pasture Park
Calf Pasture Pt
Calf Pasture Beach
Calf Pasture
Charles Cr
Gregory Pt
Peach I
Breakwater
Shoaling rep 1977
Round Beach
Raymond Rks
Grassy Hammock Rks
White Rk
Rogers Reef
Fitch Reef
Sandy Hammock
Tree Hammock
Cable Area
BETTS
Peck Ledge
GOOSE I
Chimon Rks
Beers Rocks
Copps I
Copps Rocks
Channel Rk
Haycock Rk
Dunder Rk
Yellow Rks
Little Tavern I
Seymour Rk
Bluff Pt
CANFIELD
Village Cr
Mud
Grass
Q R 26ft 4M "14"
Fl R 6s 27ft 4M "10"
Fl R 4s 26ft 5M "8"
Fl 4s 61ft 7M
G "5" GONG
Fl R 2.5s
Awash at MLLW

1868

Caisson Technology

Southwest Ledge Light, New Haven, Connecticut

Advances in caisson technology enabled Southwest Ledge Light to be constructed at the end of a breakwater in New Haven Harbor, Connecticut, marking the presence of a submerged rocky ledge at the eastern approach to the harbor. An important seaport on the Long Island Sound, as well as a local center of industry, it was—and remains—vital that vessels could gain safe access to New Haven's protected harbor. This tower replaced the 1840 New Haven Harbor Lighthouse, whose soaring octagonal masonry tower had itself supplanted a wooden tower erected in 1805 that was subsequently deemed insufficiently tall. Although, like its successor, the 1840 lighthouse was located on the eastern side of the harbor, it was an onshore beacon and did not directly provide protection from the underwater ledge. The plan for a new offshore beacon at the end of the hazardous Southwest Ledge became viable with the advent of the caisson.

The cast-iron tower destined for Southwest Ledge, which was assembled in a Baltimore, Maryland, shipyard, was not dispatched to its intended site immediately, however, being first displayed in Pennsylvania, at the 1876 Centennial Exposition hosted by Philadelphia. Its inclusion in the Exposition indicates the pride that both the Lighthouse Board and its manufacturers took in this cutting-edge, French Second-Empire-style manifestation of offshore building expertise. Transported to its breakwater site later in the year, the 45-foot (13.7-meter) tower was raised above a steel-and-concrete caisson before going into operation on New Year's Day, 1877. The structure's durability has proved equal to its elegance, and the light continues to perform a valuable function in guiding marine traffic into and away from the harbor, which is today a popular pleasure-craft destination. Although the original fourth-order Fresnel lens has since been replaced with a modern plastic optic and the beacon has been automated, the original character of the light tower—which flashes a red signal 57 feet (17.4 meters) above sea level—remains unaltered. The photograph above shows Petty Officer Mike Bero, of the U.S. Coast Guard A.N.T. Long Island Sound, on the beacon's lantern-room gallery.

Engineer's cross-section
Shown at right is the original engineer's drawing for the planned lighthouse structure to be built atop a caisson foundation at Southwest Ledge, New Haven, Connecticut. The photograph on which the drawing is superimposed shows that the lighthouse that was eventually constructed on the site in 1876 conformed closely to the engineer's sketch.

CAISSON, CRIB AND COFFERDAM LIGHTHOUSES

Some proposed offshore sites were unsuitable for any kind of screwpile lighthouse: for example, rough deep-sea locations, or sites subject to destructive moving ice flows. The screwpile lighthouses at Wolf Trap and Solomon's Lump proved unable to withstand the force of moving ice in 1893, when the first was swept away, and the latter was toppled by ice in Chesapeake Bay. By the mid to late nineteenth century, a solution to the puzzle faced by builders contemplating such locations had appeared in the form of the caisson.

In simplified terms, a caisson is a corrosion-resistant, cast-iron cylinder open at both ends. The bottom end, which has a cutting edge, is lowered to the soft ocean floor and weighed down by filling it with a ballast of rocks, sand and concrete, thus forcing out the water and transforming the caisson into a solid foundation. An alternative to this method, and one that is more suitable for uneven, or otherwise problematic, sites, is the pneumatic, or submarine-site, caisson—a box containing an airtight bulkhead (a wall-like partition, or second bottom) of concrete-covered cast iron. This creates an airlocked work chamber that construction workers reach by means of metal shafts or pipes, through which breathable air is pumped as they prepare the foundation. Additional hoses in the dredging wells extract the excavated debris as the caisson sinks farther into the seabed, extra sections being added to the top as necessary to compensate for this gradual loss of height. Once the caisson has reached a satisfactory depth—often as much as 33 feet (10 meters) below the seabed—the workmen are brought to the surface and it is filled with concrete. In both cases, the lighthouse itself is then constructed directly above the caisson, whose upper end protrudes above the high-water level. A freshwater cistern and cellar are fashioned in the top of the caisson, and the lighthouse above is usually built to a height of two or three stories.

Like many features of lighthouse technology, the caisson originated in Britain, as the brainchild of Lawrence Potts, an inventive doctor who demonstrated the potential of his idea in 1842, with a pump and a length of hollow tubing inserted into the seabed. As air

Below: Miah Maull Shoal Light, Delaware Bay, New Jersey, is a spark-plug-type lighthouse that was constructed upon a concrete caisson in open waters in 1913. The beacon, now automated, was named for Nehemiah Maull, who drowned near the site.

was pumped down the tubing, sand was forced upward, thereby driving the tubing deeper. Adopted by engineers for the erection of railroad bridges, Potts's basic caisson technology was advanced in 1850 during construction of a bridge at Rochester, New York, when water was pumped out of a length of tubing of vast diameter, and workmen then entered the tube to remove the debris at the bottom.

Because the caisson structure is so strong, these lighthouses were favored for sites that were vulnerable to moving ice, which resulted in a number of towers being constructed in both Chesapeake and Delaware Bays. Proving the caisson's ability to resist immense force, Virginia's second Wolf Trap Light has stood unscathed in Chesapeake Bay since 1893, unlike its screwpile predecessor. The style of U.S. caisson-type lighthouses varied, those in Chesapeake Bay, for example, assuming forms that recalled either handleless coffee pots, or the more elaborate architectural flights of fancy of the French Second Empire period. An example of the former style is Virginia's Newport News Middle Ground Light (1891), while the latter includes the two-story house whose mansard roof supports the lantern at Maryland's Sandy Point Shoal Light (1883). Other notable U.S. caisson lighthouses include Michigan's 130-foot (40-meter) conical steel Rock of Ages, erected on a caisson 50 feet (15 meters) wide and 30 feet (9 meters) high; Maine's near-identical "spark-plug"-style Lubec Channel Light and Goose Rocks Light (both 1890). Louisiana also boasts a spark-plug-type lighthouse at Sabine Bank (1906), which stands 15 miles (24 kilometers) offshore in the Gulf of Mexico, making it the United States' most exposed caisson lighthouse. Like Sabine Bank's light, that at Delaware's Fourteen Foot Bank (1887) was raised using the pneumatic-caisson technique—the first time that this was attempted for a lighthouse in the United States.

The Roter Sand Lighthouse, Europe's first pneumatic-caisson-type light, was erected in the estuary of Germany's Weser River in 1885, and both caisson-construction techniques were employed for many of the world's lighthouses well into the twentieth century. Trinity House engineers raised the Nab Tower Light at Bembridge Ridge, off the Isle of Wight, England, during the 1920s, and Christiani and Nielsen Ltd., of Sweden, were responsible for the beacon stationed at Kish Bank, off Ireland's eastern coast (1965). The concrete caisson that supports Kish Bank Light, which

has a diameter of 104 feet (31.7 meters), was constructed at Dún Laoghaire Harbor before being towed into position, making it a "float-out" structure. The tower's design resembles the sections of a telescope (which were extended with hydraulic jacks only after it had been positioned offshore to prevent its being damaged in transit); the lantern is topped by a helipad to enable inspection visits.

Crib (or crib-dam) and cofferdam lighthouses are both site-specific variations on the caisson theme, the crib-construction type proliferating in North America's Great Lakes and the cofferdam proving useful in relatively shallow waters. Named for its resemblance to a child's crib, or cradle, the crib used to construct such lighthouses as Spectacle Reef consisted of a framework of timbers that was fashioned ashore and then towed to the site. Here it was sunk to the lake bed or submerged-rock surface, the water that it enclosed first being pumped out and the crib then anchored in place by filling its open cavity with stones. Next the stone surface was sealed and then built up with concrete to form an above-water platform on which the super-

Below: *The caisson that supports Connecticut's coffeepot-style Greens Ledge Light (1902) was constructed at the end of the submerged ledge that extends across the entrance channel into Norwalk Harbor.*

Above: *As its name suggests, Virginia's Newport News Middle Ground Light was built above the central shoal that threatens mariners sailing along the Hampton Roads. The 35-foot (10.7-meter) lighthouse was constructed in 1891 above a substantial caisson.*

structure was erected. The story of the construction of Spectacle Reef's lighthouse, after two schooners foundered on the submerged limestone shoal in Lake Huron, Michigan, in 1867, illustrates the procedure for a crib-type lighthouse, which was carried out between 1870 and 1874 under the direction of Major Orlando Metcalfe Poe. First a circular crib 32 feet (10 meters) in diameter was constructed on land before being lowered onto the surface of the shoal, 11 feet (3 meters) below water. After the water was siphoned out of the crib, precut blocks of limestone were then bolted to the shoal to a depth of 21 inches (53 centimeters). The foundation was built up with additional courses of limestone that were secured with cement-sealed bolts. Finally, a conical masonry tower was raised to a height of 86 feet (26 meters) above the square supportive platform that had been built above the caisson, flanked by a separate dwelling and storehouse. A similar technique was also employed for the construction of many notable Great Lakes crib-type structures, including Detroit River Lighthouse, Lake Erie. Its beacon went into service in 1885 on a cast-iron conical tower with an integrated dwelling, which rested upon a concrete-filled crib enclosed by a granite pier.

Like the caisson and crib, a cofferdam traps, or dams, water within it, which is pumped away to leave a dry work site. Indeed, the similarity between the caisson and cofferdam techniques has engendered an arcane debate as to whether there is any real difference between the two. Thus one notable cofferdam lighthouse, which was constructed in 1871 in the shallow waters off Duxbury, north of Plymouth Harbor, Massachusetts, could also be termed a caisson structure. In this instance, a cofferdam in the form of a cylindrical iron tube was placed in the designated position and the water inside it removed, leaving a dry surface on which preparation was completed before filling the cofferdam with rocks and concrete. Once construction of the conical, 47-foot (14-meter) lighthouse was complete, the "bug light," as it is known locally, went into service. In Europe, an important early cofferdam-foundation light can be seen on Bishop's Rock, southwest of the Isles of Scilly, where Nicholas Douglass's team labored between 1851 and 1858 to raise the tower, which stands 120 feet (37 meters) high.

TEXAS TOWERS

During the 1960s, a new type of offshore lighthouse was erected under the auspices of the U.S. Coast Guard: the so-called Texas tower, named for its structural similarities to the oil rigs that had sprung up off the shores of the Lone Star State. In many respects, the Texas tower is descended from the straight-pile lighthouse, for both were constructed above straightpiles driven into the ocean floor. However, during the nineteenth century, the piles usually penetrated the seabed to depths of only a few feet, while their twentieth-century incarnations were driven to astonishing depths of up to 170 feet (52 meters). Steel rods were then inserted into the piles (usually four in number) and braced with a network of horizontal and diagonal crossbars beneath the surface, above which a landing platform was constructed with stairs leading first to a maintenance deck and then to dwelling level. A square tower supporting a lantern and radio beacon was generally sited in one corner of the roof, the remaining space being given over to a helipad.

Their strength and invulnerability to the most destructive hurricanes, and the facility with which they could be installed at hazardous sites, led to Texas towers replacing such lightships as the one stationed in New York City's Ambrose Channel (1967). The first Texas-tower-type beacon was constructed in Buzzards Bay, Massachusetts, in 1961; a handful of others followed later in the decade. However, the expense of constructing and maintaining these high-tech light towers proved prohibitive, and now the U. S. Coast Guard favors large navigational buoys instead. As a result, only four Texas towers survive: the Buzzards Bay Light, North Carolina's Frying Pan Shoals (1964) and Diamond Shoals Lights (1966), and Virginia's Chesapeake Light (1965), all scheduled to be dismantled. Indeed, although the world's seas and waterways still have many active offshore lighthouses, it is only a matter of time before these, too, are replaced by less costly buoys.

Above: *Dunmore East Light, off the coast of County Waterford, southeastern Ireland, which was built on a pierhead on an inlet sheltered by the Hook Head promontory.*

BREAKWATER AND PIERHEAD LIGHTS

As the names suggest, breakwater and pierhead lights stand on stone or concrete piers or breakwaters at harbor entrances and were built to guide mariners safely into waters often teeming with maritime traffic and presenting a number of natural and manmade hazards, including the piers or breakwaters themselves. In designing such structures, their architects had to ensure that they were not so heavy as to damage the foundations to which they were cemented, but strong enough to resist the force of breaking waves and the vibrations created by choppy waters. Thus many breakwater and pier lights either consisted of, or were plated in, cast iron or steel—materials lighter than masonry, highly durable and, to some extent, flexible. Peru's grandly named

Above: *The third incarnation of Rhode Island's Newport Harbor Light was raised in 1865 at the end of the Goat Island breakwater. The durability of this 35-foot (10.7-meter) granite tower was demonstrated in 1922, when it survived a submarine collision in which the keepers' residence suffered irreparable damage, but the lighthouse itself stood firm.*

Torre Reloj del Muelle de Guerra ("Watch Tower of the War Pier"), in Calloa Harbor, raised in 1889, is a good example of the pier or breakwater light tower. A conical steel tower 39 feet (12 meters) tall, it is encircled by a platform of granite and concrete at the pier's end. Four clock faces are set in its quadrangular summit—an unusual feature.

Such lighthouses were either incorporated into the pier or breakwater at the time of its construction, or were added later, often as the result of an increase in maritime traffic. Chicago Harbor Light in Illinois—a steel-plated tower flanked by a fog-signal building and boat house—was built on a mainland site at the entrance to the Chicago River in 1893 before being moved to the end of the harbor's northern breakwater in 1919. Sometimes a new light was required, as when the trapezoidal tower built on Maine's Rockland Harbor Breakwater at the time of its construction in 1888 was replaced after the breakwater was lengthened, by a dwelling-type station atop a granite pier (1902). Although it was first assembled in 1876, Connecticut's cast-iron Southwest Ledge Light (a caisson-foundation type, 45 feet, or 14 meters tall) was not erected on New Haven's eastern breakwater until 1877 for a different reason: it was displayed at the Centennial Exposition in Philadelphia, after which it was reassembled above a dangerous submerged ledge in Long Island Sound.

Generally constructed of cast iron, the superstructures of pier and breakwater lighthouses display a multitude of forms. Those of the Great Lakes, for example, boast a plethora of architectural styles, ranging from solitary towers to basic one-and-one-half-story integrated dwellings to over-the-top Victorian fantasies. New York State's third Sodus Point Pierhead Lighthouse (1901) is a square tower perched at the end of a concrete pier that jutts into Sodus Bay, while Michigan's Muskegon South Pier Light (1903) is similarly economical: a conical cast-iron tower painted red to make it an effective daymark. In contrast to the Grand Marais Lighthouse, Minnesota (1922), which consists simply of a pyramidal dwelling level and lantern perched above four steel piles, Ohio's Ashtabula Lighthouse (1916) resembles a respectable, if isolated, house, as does New York State's third Oswego West Pierhead Light (1934), at the end of a concrete pier on a stone breakwater in Oswego Harbor, Lake Ontario. More elaborate lighthouse confections include Ohio's Lorain and Toledo Harbor Lights, both built on Lake Erie breakwaters. The elegant townhouselike Lorain Light, which was constructed above a concrete and rubblestone foundation in

Above: *Until 1898 Crete, the largest and southernmost of the Greek islands, was under Turkish rule, whose architectural influence is apparent in this lighthouse on the breakwater that protects Khania's Venetian Harbor.*

Left: *The first breakwater at the ancient harbor of Akko, Israel, was built as early as the fifth century* BC. *The "Tower of Flies" Light today stands guard over the entrance to the modern fishing harbor.*

Above: Indiana's Michigan City East Pier Light was constructed on a concrete platform at the end of the East Pier in 1904. Taking the form of a pyramidal-roofed, steel-encased brick dwelling, through the center of which an octagonal tower protrudes, this configuration is common to many Great Lakes lighthouses.

Piers or breakwaters may support more than one lighthouse. Two beacons with lanterns at different levels often act as range lights, whose alignment signals a safe passage, as seen on Michigan's Grand Haven South and St. Joseph North Piers. When the 1895 pier at the entrance to Grand Haven River was extended in 1905, the shedlike building that housed the light station's fog 1917, belies its thick walls of steel and concrete, while the brick facing of the elaborate crib-foundation Toledo Harbor Light (1904) comprises a riot of architectural conventions, from the Romanesque to the French Second Empire. Perhaps one of the most unusual U.S. breakwater lighthouses is the uncompromisingly spare structure centered on San Pedro Middle Breakwater, Los Angeles. The epitome of Modernist architecture, Long Beach Harbor Light (1949) consists of two different-sized, rectangular concrete levels standing above six vast concrete legs sunk into the breakwater—a design intended to protect it against earthquake damage.

signal was separated from the cylindrical tower and promoted to the status of a lighthouse. On its removal to the end of the pier, it was clad in cast iron to help it survive Lake Michigan's ferocious storm waves. Connected by a raised walkway, the range lights of St. Joseph's North Pier were erected in 1907; the pierhead, or front-range, light, is a conical tower, while the rear-range light is an octagonal structure with a lantern protruding from its roof. The latter resembles Michigan City, Indiana's, East Pier Light (1904), among other similar structures.

Although beacons on monopoles have supplemented such lighthouses in recent years, they remain important daymarks and still offer a welcome sight to weary mariners nearing their journey's end.

Below: *From its commanding position on a solidly constructed breakwater, the lighthouse at Bangor, County Down, guides vessels through the waters of Northern Ireland's Belfast Lough, an inlet of the Irish Sea.*

OPTICAL APPARATUS

Lighting and Lens Technology

Previous pages: *North Head Light, at the northern approach to the Columbia River, Washington, received a first-order Fresnel lens upon its completion in 1898. Its replacement of 1939, a fourth-order lens, was in turn superseded by an aerobeacon.*

Below: *The first-order Fresnel lens at Cape Meares Light, Oregon, in the setting sun. The light was deactivated in 1963, and its lens was later vandalized.*

Although lighthouses may perform an important role as daymarks in fine weather simply through their looming presence, in dark, foggy, or stormy conditions their outlines may be obscured. That is why, since earliest times, the lighting of a beacon has been a vital aid to navigation for mariners approaching the shore at night, or in bad weather, either warning them away from a natural hazard or providing a visible focus upon which to set their course. Unfortunately, throughout history, sailors' reliance on such beacons to facilitate their safe passage was all too often abused by "wreckers," the unscrupulous entrappers whose greed prompted them to place lights at locations that were certain to result in the wreckage of vessels and thus a rich crop of cargo, as well as flotsam and jetsam that could be used as building materials. Nevertheless, beacons had to be lit, and mariners often had little choice but to put their faith in them. Such fears gradually became a thing of the past as lighthouse authorities around the world announced the completion of successive generations of lights.

Four fundamental elements had to be considered when raising a beacon: its elevation,

the nature of the light itself, the fuel that it used, and the best way to maximize the effectiveness of the beam. In the days of prehistory, when people had next to no technology at their disposal, they aided their seafaring folk by any means they could. The earliest beacons are believed to have been simple bonfires, kindled either on the seashore or on a bluff. Although the Romans were among the first to erect permanent light towers, they, too, had to place unprotected wood fires at their summits, forcing light keepers to fight a constant battle against wind and rain to nurse a guttering flame back to life, or to kindle another.

Slow progress was made over the millennia with the introduction of coal, candles and covered lanterns, which on the one hand provided a ready, and relatively enduring, light source, and, on the other, a protective housing for the vulnerable flame. Glazing the lantern represented another step forward, but because thick layers of soot built up unrelentingly on the glass panes, they had to be cleaned regularly and meticulously to ensure the light's visibility. Indeed, the British Royal Navy frequently encouraged the careless keepers of Nova Scotia's Sambro Island Lighthouse (1758) to clean their lantern room by the unusual, but effective, expedient of firing cannon balls in their direction.

Over the centuries, methods of fueling the illuminant progressed from wood and coal fires through spermaceti, colza (rapeseed), lard and mineral oil (kerosene or paraffin), all of which were in use during the nineteenth century. The twentieth century saw the prevalence of incandescent oil-vapor lamps and electric bulbs, sometimes solar-powered. However, the effectiveness of all of these illuminants—whatever their energy source—was in themselves limited, for unless their light was focused into a concentrated beam, it was too diffuse to provide a useful aid to navigation in murky conditions. Mirrors and parabolic reflectors used in partnership with Argand lamps provided a partial solution to this problem, but it was not until the invention of the Fresnel lens during the early nineteenth century that the lighthouse beam became powerful and efficient. This chapter tracks the evolution of lighting and lens technology, whose primary function is to illuminate the beacon upon which mariners depend for their survival.

Above: *The first-order Fresnel lens at Point Sur Light, Big Sur, California, guided mariners away from the hazards of this precipitous coast from 1889 until 1972, when it was replaced by an aerobeacon, which, like its predecessor, emits a flash every fifteen seconds.*

THE ELEVATION OF THE LIGHT

In classical times it was already understood that the Earth's curvature affects the movement of light over distance. In order to be visible out at sea, a light source must be as elevated as possible.

A light placed 10 feet (3 meters) above sea level can be seen up to 9.2 statute, or "terrestrial," miles (8 nautical miles or 14.8 kilometers) out to sea, its range increasing to 31 miles (21 nautical miles, or 38.9 kilometers) when it is 200 feet (61 meters) above sea level. A light tower built on a cliff has the benefit of a naturally elevated position and need not be a tall structure, but where the shoreline is flat, a tall tower is needed to attain the necessary height. These principles are illustrated by two examples. Despite the diminutive height of South Korea's Ongdo Light (1904), which is only 46 feet (14 meters) tall, because it stands atop a cliff, its light is projected to great distances over the Yellow Sea. By contrast, Estonia's Pakri Lighthouse (1889), whose location does not have this advantage, was built to a height of 171 feet (52 meters) to make it function as an efficient aid to mariners navigating the Baltic Sea. Although the light beam itself may not be directly visible because of the Earth's curvature, a powerful light source may create a "loom," or "lume," effect, by which water vapor in the atmosphere diffuses the light upward to form a halo above the lantern.

Right: Tiritiri Matangi Island Lighthouse, New Zealand, houses a powerful xenon-discharge lamp.

These general principles do not dictate that lighthouses should soar to unlimited heights, however. In fog-bound areas, highly elevated lights are frequently obscured: for this reason, a number of lighthouses have been rebuilt with their light at an elevation lower than the original, below the fog line, including Point Bonita Light, California, and Ireland's Old Head of Kinsale Lighthouse.

Fog and low cloud also affect the intensity requirements of a light source. Although modern lights may have a luminous intensity as low as 100,000 candelas (today's standard international unit of measurement, derived from the strength of the light from a standard candle, or its candlepower), which is visible for 23 miles (20 nautical miles, or 37 kilometers) in clear weather, when the prevailing atmospheric conditions are unfavorable, a higher luminous intensity is needed to compensate for atmospheric filtration. In 1956, for example, it became necessary to equip New Zealand's Tiritiri Matangi Island Lighthouse (1865) with an extraordinarily powerful 10-million-candela xenon-discharge lamp. In marked contrast, the relatively fair-weather location of Italy's San Raineri Lighthouse (1857), in Messina, means that a mere 26,000 candelas is sufficient to give the light its required range.

LIGHT SOURCES, FUEL AND REFLECTORS

When it first went into service in 1290, Spain's Porto Pi Lighthouse, on the island of Majorca, relied on locally obtainable olive oil to produce its light. However, light keepers of the colder climes of northern Europe continued to burn wood until well into the eighteenth century, although from the mid-sixteenth century, coal—a compact, carbonaceous fossil fuel that burns more slowly than wood and produces a brighter, longer-lasting flame—began to be preferred. The coal was piled into a basketlike metal brazier or grate, which could either be placed at the apex of a light tower, or form part of a basic lever light, or vippefyr, named by its seventeenth-century Danish inventor Jens Pedersen Groves. Introduced to lighthouse duty at about the same time as coal, candles provided a lighter, cleaner and more easily maintained alternative. Perhaps surprisingly, the construction of a lantern at the top of the tower to enclose and protect the naked flame from the elements was often a relatively late innovation: Ireland's Hook Head Lighthouse, which dates back to 1172, did not receive one until 1791.

One of the perpetual problems of using a naked flame of any sort—particularly if the lighthouse was constructed of timber or contained wooden components—was the danger that it would burn out of control and destroy the lighthouse itself, a fate that befell numerous towers, including John Rudyerd's second Eddystone Light (1709) in 1755. Another obstacle to the light's effectiveness was the prodigious amount of soot-laden smoke produced by the burning process, which quickly coated the lantern's glass and dimmed the brightness of the light as seen from afar. This problem was not solved by the installation of spider lamps—pans of oil containing four to ten wicks—which many U.S. lighthouses installed during the 1790s, and the irritating fumes they produced made the keeper's job almost unendurable.

Left: The open fire atop Dungeness Light, near Dover, England, in a 1699 illustration.

The patenting of a smokeless light in 1784 by its inventor Aimé Argand, a Swiss scientist, represented a significant improvement in the keeper's lot, as well as a landmark in the history of lighthouse illuminants. A vital component of Argand's invention was the glass chimney, which provided updraft—and thus oxygen—to the flame that was produced when a coiled wick contained in a metal tube was lit, drawing fuel from a reservoir of oil. With the wick burning off the oxygen on either side of it, the Argand lamp produced a steady smoke-free light, whose strength equaled that of seven candles, but did not create such sooty lantern-room conditions. The problem of light diffusion remained, however, and when the English lighthouse authority, Trinity House, first introduced the Argand lamp, it drew upon earlier experiments with mirrors and reflectors and augmented the lamp with a sheet of silvered copper hammered into a parabolic (ogival) shape. When this movable parabolic reflector was placed behind the lamp, with the

Above: America's oldest lighthouse, Boston Harbor Light, Massachusetts, has hosted a variety of lighting apparatus since its completion in 1716, including the Argand-inspired lamp-and-reflector system that was first demonstrated here by Winslow Lewis in 1810.

Opposite: An isolated light station near Bergen, Norway (see gatefold feature).

flame positioned at its focal point, it obstructed the passage of the light and reflected it back again, thereby enabling keepers to focus the light to increase its effective candlepower by a factor of about 400 and to obtain an optimal beam from the equipment.

Although experiments with early versions of this catoptric system, to give it its technical name, had been carried out by a handful of people prior to the advent of the Argand lamp, the unsteadiness of the beam produced by the naked flame had made it unreliable. At Scotland's Bell Rock Lighthouse (1811), Robert Stevenson successfully introduced a revolving mechanism, as well as another modification by mounting lamps and reflectors on movable square chandeliers and covering two opposite sides with red glass. When the apparatus was rotated, the light appeared to flash white and red, thereby identifying it as that projected by the Bell Rock tower.

Led by Britain and France, the Argand lamp-and-reflector system rapidly became the favored illuminant of most national lighthouse authorities and remained in general use well into the second half of the nineteenth century, fueled progressively by different types of oil. One of the many British towers equipped with Argand lamps and reflectors was Wales's South Stack Lighthouse (1809), off Anglesey's Holyhead Island. This light reportedly inspired the former American sea captain Winslow Lewis to lobby for the right to install a similar illumination system in U.S. lighthouses. Seizing an opportunity to enrich himself, Lewis demonstrated his version of Argand's oil-burning apparatus and reflectors (to which he added a light-focusing lens like that used at South Stack) at Boston and Cape Ann Lights in Massachusetts. The superiority of Lewis's equipment over the spider lamps was clear, and in 1810 Congress authorized the purchase of his patent for $60,000 and authorized him to install and maintain his reflectors and lamps in all of the U.S. lighthouses (then numbering forty-nine).

Despite being a vast improvement on the spider lamps, Lewis's system was by no means ideal. First, the green-tinted lens that he placed in front of the illuminant partially blocked the passage of the light, and, secondly, his reflectors were easily damaged by cleaning. Although the U.S. lighthouse inspectors appointed by Congress lamented the general state of Lewis's lights in 1838, by 1851 they were used in all but three American lighthouses. Not only did their relative cheapness appeal to the penny-pinching fifth auditor Stephen Pleasanton, but his loyalty to—or collusion with—Lewis made him indifferent to possible alternatives.

(continued on page 158)

A Clifftop Sentinel

The headland upon which Kilauea Point Light was raised commands a breathtaking view over the Pacific Ocean, as seen in the photograph above. Although the beacon, which stands on Hawaii's Kauai Island, is only 53 feet (16.2 meters) in height, its site has a natural elevation of 180 feet (54.9 meters), and the new light's focal plane is an impressive 216 feet (65.8 meters) above sea level. Volcanic activity was responsible for Kilauea Point's height (the volcano is still active today), and the lighthouse that sits atop it is an important one: it is the northernmost light on the Hawaiian archipelago and fulfills a significant function in acting as a making light for mariners sailing from Eastern ports. A myriad of isolated volcanic rocks stud the coastline, as can be seen in the panoramic view at right, and the powerful Pacific surf pounds the archipelago constantly, making for dangerous conditions for vessels in these waters. When it was first lit, in 1913, the lighthouse was equipped with a powerful second-order Fresnel lens, which was replaced by an aerobeacon upon the light station's automation in 1976.

Elevated Lights

Many of the world's landfall, or "making," lighthouses need only be diminutive in height to achieve the required range, since their sites give them the advantage of natural elevation. This equation is demonstrated by the majority of the lighthouses—including the light station pictured on the previous page, off Bergen—that have been constructed on Norway's numerous offshore islands, whose rocky terrain was created by glacial movement.

The soaring locations of several Quebec lighthouses, including Bird Rock Island Lighthouse (above), are the product of the formation eons ago of the Canadian Shield and Appalachian Mountains. Wilson's Promontory, which forms the southernmost tip of Victoria, Australia's southwesternmost state, provides a similarly commanding location for the Southeast Point Lighthouse (below).

Low-lying Sites

Light towers on low-lying sites must be tall in order to enable their signals to be seen up to 25 miles (40 kilometers) out to sea. The second Assateague Island Light, Virginia (overleaf), was raised to a height of 142 feet (43.3 meters) in 1867, giving its first-order Fresnel lens a focal plane of 154 feet (47 meters) above sea level. The low-lying Loggerhead Key, on which Florida's Dry Tortugas Light (below) was constructed in 1858, similarly demanded a tall structure to guide mariners safely away from the surrounding shoals: the building reaches a height of 157 feet (47.8 meters). The Westerhever Light (above), in the German state of Schleswig-Holstein, towers above the "Wadden Sea," a vast, flat salt-water marsh that was created by glacial activity at the end of the Ice Age.

Anatomy of the Fresnel Lens

Heceta Head Light, Oregon

The lantern room at Oregon's Heceta Head Lighthouse still boasts the original first-order lens that was installed here in 1894. The overlay on page 1 shows the lens detail. The largest of the seven orders, first-order lenses are typically 12 feet (3.7 meters) tall and have a diameter of 6 feet (1.8 meters). These giant lenses consist of hundreds, if not a thousand, individual pieces of glass or plastic that are assembled within a metal framework to form an intricate housing for the light, the lens components focusing the beam to its optimum efficiency. When a flashing characteristic is required, as here, the entire lens is rotated by clockwork. Arranged above and below the central panel, concentric lens rings and prisms capture any "stray" beams of light, refracting them toward the beam, concentrating and magnifying the light into a powerful single signal beam. Once containing multiwicked, oil-fueled lamps at their epicenters, advances in technology have meant that today's surviving Fresnel lenses are usually powered by electric light bulbs.

Below: Located on the Avalon Peninsula, Newfoundland's Cape Race Light was equipped with a massive hyperradiant lens in 1906 in the lantern room of the second lighthouse to stand at this site. Typically measuring 16 feet (5 meters) in height, and with a diameter of 8 feet, 8 inches (2.6 meters), the hyperradiant lens is relatively rare.

THE FRESNEL LENS

In their report on U.S. lighthouses in 1851, the investigating commissioners included a damning verdict: "The illuminating apparatus in the United States is of a description now nearly obsolete throughout all maritime countries." Effectively recommending that Lewis's lights and reflectors be consigned to the trash can of history, they advocated installation of the Fresnel lens already used in European lighthouses for nearly thirty years.

A civil engineer employed by the French lighthouse authority since 1813, Augustin-Jean Fresnel's primary interest was the nearly infant science of optics. Having studied, and become intrigued by, the work of such scientists as Georges-Louis Leclerc de Buffon and Antoine de Condorcet, both of whom had advanced early lens technology by devising compound lenses consisting of a series of concentric, prismatic, glass rings, Fresnel set about refining their theories, and by 1822 had produced his prototypical eponymous lens. Simply put, this glass lens consisted of a central lens at the center of several concentric circular prisms, giving the whole lens panel a grooved appearance. When the lens panel was placed in front of the illuminant (making it a dioptric rather than a catoptric system), triangular prisms placed at the top and bottom of the concentric rings caught the light radiated outward by the illuminant and refracted, or bent, it toward the beam, thereby concentrating the light into a horizontal signal and increasing its luminous intensity. Fresnel had solved the problem of light diffusion that had plagued lighthouse builders for centuries. Unlike the contemporaneous, prohibitively heavy, solid lenses, not only was Fresnel's lens remarkably light, but its components could also be transported separately to the lighthouse, where they were reassembled in the lantern room itself—an enormous boon in the case of towers that were hundreds of feet high. Just as important, however, was its luminous intensity, which was four times that of the Argand lamp-and-reflector system.

In practice, an oil lamp very similar to Argand's, with one to five circular, concentric wicks, was placed at the center of a cylindrical brass frame containing four lens panels that together formed a drum lens. A fixed light was produced by a belt consisting of a continuous lens about the center. The combination of a central bull's-eye lens and a rotational apparatus enabled the lighthouse to display a flashing light, the flash being produced by blocking the passage of the light with solid panels, and flashing colors, by using colored glass panels. Stray light could be redirected by a fanlike arrangement of mirrors above it, like those on which Fresnel and Alan Stevenson collaborated for Skerryvore Lighthouse (1842). Despite their comparative lightness, Fresnel lenses could weigh as much as 5 tons and stand 12 feet (3.7 meters) tall, so to rotate them easily and safely, they were either mounted upon a turntable revolved on ball bearings, as can still be seen at Spain's Porto Pi Lighthouse, or floated in a cast-iron container filled with mercury, which enabled frictionless movement. [Mercury's toxicity was unknown at the time, and where mercury baths are still used today, as at Senegal's Mamelles Lighthouse (1864) and England's Casquets (1724), the substance is safely contained.] Power was initially supplied by hand-wound clockwork, a weight being lowered to set the gears that rotated the turntable in motion.

Above: *This interior shot of the first-order Fresnel lens at Point Reyes Light, California (1870), affords a view of the rotational mechanism that produced the light's flashing white character until 1975, when its function was assumed by a modern optic mounted on a nearby fog-signal building.*

Because the requirements of individual lighthouses differed appreciably from one another, Fresnel designed six orders of lenses, designated by the numbers one to six (a seventh, the three-and-a-half order, was developed later). The order of the lens was determined by its focal length, or the distance between the flame produced by the lamp and the surface of the lens, which in turn influenced the size of the lens itself. First-order Fresnel lenses had the longest focal distance and were the largest: up to 12 feet (3.7 meters) high and 6 feet (1.8 meters) in diameter, their light could be seen 20 miles (32 kilometers) out to sea. These, as well as the progressively smaller second- and third-order lenses, were suited to coastal locations, while the less demanding conditions of river, bay and harbor sites were met by the relatively diminutive fourth-, fifth- and sixth-order lenses. During the late nineteenth century, Tom Stevenson, one of Robert Stevenson's sons, developed a dioptric holophotal light, the forerunner of the giant hyperradiant lens, whose focal distance was 52 inches (132 centimeters) to the first-order lens's 36 inches (92 centimeters). After being displayed at Chicago's World's Columbian Exposition (1893), the hyperradiant lens went into service at Makapuu Point Lighthouse, on Oahu, Hawaii, in 1909. The only such lens installed in a U.S. tower, it has a diameter of 8 feet, 8 inches (2.6 meters) and is 16 feet (5 meters) tall. Now automated, Makapuu Point's hyperradiant lens still functions today.

Fresnel installed his first lens in the lantern room of the historic French lighthouse at Cordouan in 1823. Such was its success that

The Significance of the Fresnel Lens

The development of lenses, which refract, or bend, light, would revolutionize lighthouse technology. Problems were experienced when early lenses were used in lighthouses, however. Each lens was more than 6 feet (2 meters) high, perhaps 3 feet (1 meter) across, and about 18 inches (50 centimeters) thick. Because of their weight, a lantern's support structure had to be substantial, and further problems were caused when the expansion of the glass through heat caused cracking and breakage. Installation and rotation were also difficult.

It was clear that the lens had to be made lighter. Although its weight was almost halved by cutting it down the middle, colored fringes were added to the beam as a result. This chromatic aberration of colors confused navigators, and the lens was grossly inefficient. The necessary decrease in lens mass together with improved optical efficiency became available only with the invention of the Fresnel lens.

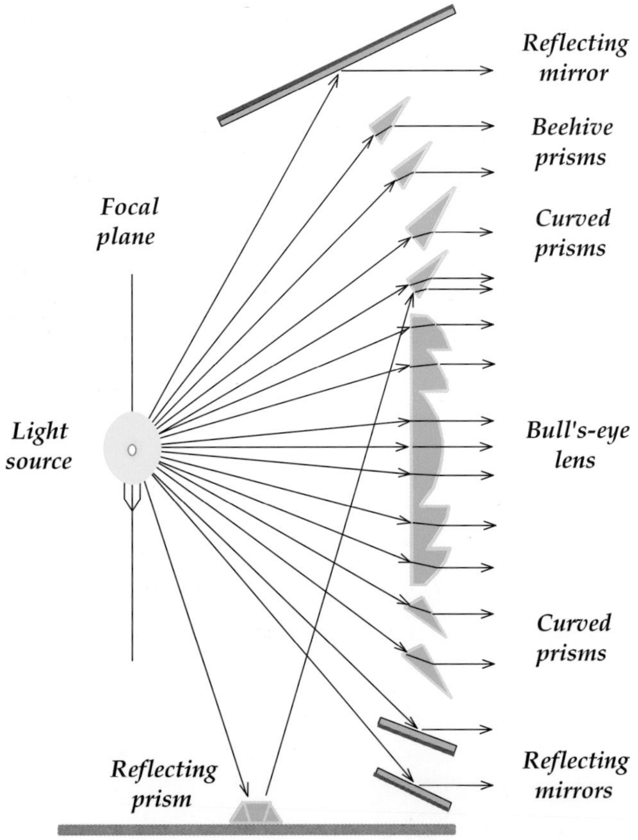

Reflecting mirror
Beehive prisms
Focal plane
Curved prisms
Light source
Bull's-eye lens
Curved prisms
Reflecting prism
Reflecting mirrors

LIGHT-PATH DIAGRAM BY GLENN O. MYERS

Born in Broglie, France, in 1788, Augustin-Jean Fresnel matured as an engineer before concentrating on the growing science of optics. Influenced by the pioneering work of the French scientists Georges-Louis Leclerc de Buffon and Antoine de Condorcet, who had experimented with concentric lenses and prismatic cross-sections, Fresnel realized that the effective functioning of a lens was more dependent upon contour than upon bulk. In his 1822 invention, he simply removed the excess glass to leave a series of concentric ridges, or grooves, each of which served as part of the larger lens. Although he reduced the weight of the lens by a factor of about ten, its optical efficiency remained undiminished. Each groove of glass could also be molded and ground individually, transported with relative ease and replaced more readily if necessary.

Fresnel's prototypical glass lens was first used as a fixed (nonflashing) collimator, or beam-focusing mechanism, at Cordouan Lighthouse near Bordeaux, France, in 1824. Its low level of light absorption and large aperture were particularly important in maximizing the weak light source that was then available. Fresnel achieved a 70 percent capture of the available light, which was then focused into a pencil beam.

Today Fresnel lenses are divided into seven strengths, or orders (focal lengths). Long focal-length lenses are found in first- and second-order lighthouses, where their greater power-handling capacity is better suited to longer-range beams. Small orders, such as fifth or sixth, are best suited to the smaller lights that are commonly found at harbor entrances and breakwater heads.

The lightweight design of Fresnel's lens also meant that it was easier to move a series of lenses to produce the effect of flashing. By supporting several of Fresnel's grooved glasses on rollers, and adding a clockwork (later, electrical) mechanism that rotated the assembly at a set and constant rate, regular, high-intensity flashing became obtainable from relatively low-intensity sources of light.

—Jem Smallwood, *Physicist*

the lighthouse authorities of France, England and Scotland rapidly placed orders for similar lenses from Fresnel's manufacturer, Soleil. In the United States, Congress dispatched Commodore Matthew C. Perry to France in 1838 to acquire sample Fresnel lenses for evaluation. As a result, in 1841 a French mechanic installed and lighted a fixed first-order lens and a flashing second-order lens at Navesink's (or Highland's) two New Jersey towers (1828), the first-order lens in the northern tower, and the second-order in the southern. The installation of a second-order Fresnel lens in the lighthouse at Sankaty Head, Massachusetts, and a third-order lens in Delaware's Brandywine Shoal lantern room soon followed. Following the investigating board's report on the state of U.S. lighthouses in 1851, and the consequent removal of Pleasanton from his administrative duties, Congress charged the newly appointed Lighthouse Board with installing Fresnel lenses, when practicable, in all American light towers—a mammoth task that was nevertheless completed within ten years.

Above: *This first-order Fresnel lens, photographed at Edgartown Museum, Martha's Vineyard, Massachusetts, spent its working life at the nearby Gay Head Light until its decommissioning in 1952. It was one of the first to be installed in a U.S. light tower in the site's second beacon in 1856, red glass panels coloring its signal.*

FUELING THE LENSES

Some European and U.S. lighthouses employed natural gas to illuminate their lights, but there were problems associated with this fuel: unless the expensive option of installing a coal-gasification plant was adopted, there had to be a naturally occurring source of gas nearby—and such a source would eventually become exhausted. Three years after New York State's Barcelona, or Portland, Light, which overlooks Lake Erie, was raised in 1829, it was discovered that a local spring gave off hydrogen gas, which was then diverted to the tower by means of a 2-mile (3-kilometer) wooden pipe, which fueled thirteen specially designed lamps. However, the gas ran out in 1838, and the lighthouse was decommissioned in 1859. Spermaceti oil, extracted from the heads of sperm whales and considered a more reliable fuel, was initially used to illuminate both the Argand and Lewis lamps, as well as Fresnel lenses in Europe and the United States. However, its increasing expense led 1840s lighthouse engineers to seek a cheaper alternative. France and Britain introduced colza oil, a rapeseed derivative, but this crop was almost unknown in the United States. Lard oil became the fuel of choice for U.S. lighthouses during the 1860s, until coal oil (kerosene or paraffin) supplanted it. The Navesink towers (rebuilt in 1862) had the first first-order lens to use this fuel, in 1883, after its introduction at lighthouses with smaller lenses in 1878. Although mineral oil produced a clean and bright flame, its volatility and inflammability were drawbacks, representing as they did a significant danger to keepers' safety.

The late nineteenth century was an era of experimentation with fuel for lighthouses, and no single source prevailed. Even as various oils were being tested and adopted, England installed an experimental electricity generator and carbon-arc lamps in the lighthouse at Dungeness, Kent, in 1862. This followed comparative trials between electric and colza-oil lights conducted in 1858 by Michael Faraday, the inventor of electromagnetic induction, at South Foreland Light, Kent. The twin Navesink lights were not only the first to receive Fresnel lenses, but they also pioneered electricity in U.S. lighthouses in 1898, when the southern tower was equipped with a bivalve electric-arc 25-million-candela lens with a range of 25 miles (40 kilometers). Electricity had also been employed at New York City's landmark Statue of Liberty since 1886.

However, it was not until power lines sprang up over increasingly industrialized nations that the majority of lighthouses were electrified, starting with that at South Foreland in 1922. Until the electrification program was completed, the incandescent oil-vapor burner, which was invented by a Briton, Arthur Kitson, and was improved by England's Trinity House engineers, provided a popular alternative illuminant from the late nineteenth into the twentieth centuries. The bright and steady light emitted by the burner was created by pressurizing kerosene, mixing it with air in a vaporizer chamber, and then burning it through wicks under an incandescent mantle.

Below: The aerobeacon that replaced the original Fresnel lens in 1957 can be seen in the lantern room of New York's Tarrytown Lighthouse (1883, decommissioned 1961), on the Hudson River, shown here with the lights of the Tappan Zee Bridge in the background.

Above: Since 1859 the light of the third Cape May, New Jersey, light tower has displayed a flashing white character. At 165 feet (50.3 meters) above sea level, the light beam that is projected a distance of 19 miles (30.6 kilometers) from the northeastern entrance to Delaware Bay is today emitted by an aerobeacon rather than the original first-order Fresnel lens.

A notable advance in the fueling of illuminants was made by Nils Gustaf Dalén, the winner of the Nobel Prize for physics in 1912, who patented his dissolved-acetylene gas burner in 1906. With his introduction of the acetylene-absorbing substance Agamassan, Dalén produced a form of acetylene that was less flammable and could thus be safely contained in storage cylinders, making it ideal for lighthouse purposes. The stability of the modified gas also meant that it was easily controlled, and the intense flame that acetylene produced was eminently suited to lighthouse illumination. The dissolved acetylene could be mixed with air and burned over an incandescent mantle, and because it generated its own pressure it could be used to power the rotational apparatus that turned the Fresnel lens, too.

The device for which Dalén, an indefatigable inventor, was awarded the Nobel Prize was the Solventil, an automatic sun valve. The Solventil incorporated a dull, black, heat-absorbing surface and a shiny, light, heat-resisting surface, as well as a switch connected to an acetylene-gas valve. Able to differentiate between night and day through the presence, or absence, of the Sun's heat, the valve automatically switched

Inside the Lens Room

St. John's Point, County Down, Northern Ireland

The lighthouse at St. John's Point, on the eastern coast of County Down, Northern Ireland, overlooking the Irish Sea, has kept pace with technological improvements throughout its history. When it was first lit, in 1844, oil was burned to produce the light, but this was superseded by coal gas, which was supplied from a nearby plant, in 1875. In common with many contemporaneous lighthouses, in 1909 incandescent oil-vapor burners were installed, which served until 1981, when the principal light was finally electrified (although the lower, auxiliary light, to which it was easier to gain access, had been powered by electricity since 1957), enabling the full automation of the light station. Today the biform lens of the main light emits two flashes every 7.5 seconds, a pattern that was retained in 1909 when the color was changed from red to white, signifying a return to the original color before its conversion to red in 1860. By contrast, the auxiliary light, which was first illuminated in 1893, has always exhibited red and white beams, although it was converted from a fixed to a flashing light in 1982.

1 *The glazed lantern room, protected by helical bars, commands an unobstructed view over the Irish Sea.*

2 *The primary electrical illuminant, seen here from inside the lens, has an intensity of 423,000 candelas.*

3 *Bull's-eye lenses magnify the light beam, while the surrounding concentric rings refract and concentrate the light to produce a more intense beam.*

4 *The revolving mechanism below the lens system enables the light to exhibit a flashing character.*

Below: Standing 100 feet (30.5 meters) above sea level, the solar-powered lighthouse at Negril, Jamaica, is the tallest structure in the city.

itself on at night, opening its gas valve to release the fuel for the illuminant, and switching it off during the day. Dalén also designed the automatic mantle-exchanger, which replaced a burned-out mantle with a fresh one. When harnessed to acetylene, such mechanisms meant that for the first time unmanned buoys could be lit and certain lighthouses automated.

ELECTRIFICATION AND AUTOMATION

Acetylene is still used to illuminate many aids to navigation (primarily buoys, although Denmark's Baagoe Lighthouse, among others, is still acetylene-lit) when is it impossible to connect them to electricity. However, the ubiquity of electricity has resulted in electrification of most of the world's lighthouses, completing a process that began in early in the twentieth century.

Electric power today is generally supplied from the national grid, with diesel-powered generators or battery-storage systems providing either a backup in the event of power failure, or the primary power supply, as at South Korea's Pudo and Ongdo Lighthouses (both 1904). Some lighthouses use solar-cell panels, in conjunction with either backup diesel generators or batteries. Other lights, like the one at Kéréon (1916), off the coast of Brittany, France, are lit by means of wind-powered generators.

The typical modern illuminant is the electric-filament light bulb that was widely introduced during the 1920s, the heating effect of the electric current that passes through the tungsten-alloy filament creating a powerful incandescent light of 5 to 1,500 watts. In 1966 when the incandescent oil-vapor burner at Singapore's Horsburgh Lighthouse was replaced with a 1,000-watt bulb, its intensity was tripled to 449,000 candelas. At such lighthouses as that at Pulau Undan (1876), in Malaysia, a series of halogen lamps and parabolic reflectors was installed, while intensely bright, xenon-discharge lamps also constitute a light source.

Although some remain in situ, like Cove Island Lighthouse's original second-order lens (installed in 1859), which projects its beam over Lake Huron from the shores of Ontario, glass Fresnel lenses have frequently been supplanted. Their successors are the lighter, and less fragile, transparent-plastic lenses, molded according to the Fresnel design, that contain up to six small light bulbs driven by an electric motor that may be turned on and off automatically to produce the flash or eclipse. Aerobeacons—rotating signals of the type used at airports—have also been installed at such towers as Cape Cod (or Highland) Light (1857) in Massachusetts, which lost its first-order Fresnel lens in 1945, as did Virginia's Cape Island Light (1895) in 1963. The lightness of the plastic lenses means that only a small platform, or, for an elevated position, a monopole, is needed to support them.

Because their performance and status can be monitored remotely by means of a telephone, radio, or satellite-communications linkup to a central computerized control station serving a number of lights, many automated lighthouses receive human visitors only rarely.

Left: *Although it is dwarfed by Two Harbors' primary lighthouse, the Two Harbors East Breakwater Light, Minnesota, fulfills just as important a navigational function, standing as it does at the end of a breakwater 25 feet (7.6 meters) above the waters of Lake Superior. Modern optical equipment and automation have made basic beacons like this cheap to build and easy to maintain.*

Left: *The advent of electrification, and hence automation, has proved a boon for lighthouse authorities charged with maintaining isolated lighthouses, such as Norway's Flavar Light. Automated lights rarely need keepers, and require only occasional inspection visits to ensure that their equipment is functioning efficiently.*

NANTUCKET

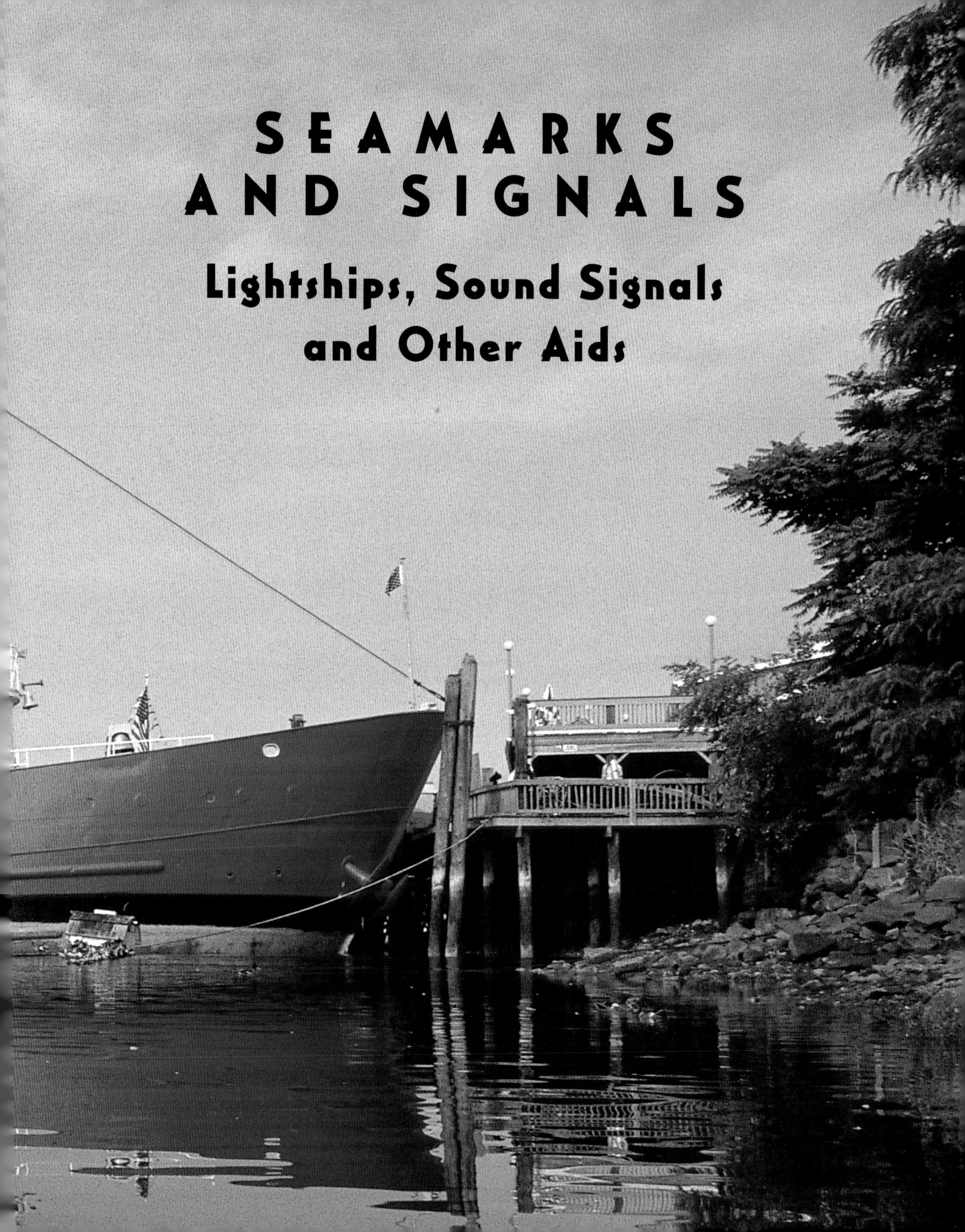
SEAMARKS
AND SIGNALS
Lightships, Sound Signals
and Other Aids

Previous pages: *Just as many lighthouses are decorated with bold patterns to improve their visibility as daymarks, so the hulls of U.S. lightships, including* Lightship No. 112, Nantucket, *were painted red to enable mariners to identify them more easily.*

Numerous aids to navigation are at the disposal of mariners today, from lighthouses, lightships, buoys and fog signals to high-tech radio beacons and racons and the satellite wizardry of the Global Positioning System (GPS). Yet despite the development of increasingly sophisticated communications systems during the twentieth century, which radically transformed methods of marine navigation, centuries-old aids still have an important role to play in safeguarding both vessels and their crews.

Even when the beacons on certain lighthouses have been decommissioned, the tower itself may still serve as a daymark—a feature visible by day from which sailors can determine their location, both by sight and by reference to nautical charts on which it is marked. Both active and decommissioned lighthouses may also be identifiable by their external markings. For instance, the black-and-white horizontal bands of New York City's second Fire Island Lighthouse of 1858 (deactivated in 1973 and now a museum), still make this 180-foot (55-meter) conical tower a marker for vessels approaching New York's busy harbor. Painting a tall coastal lighthouse in such a way makes it stand out from the monochromatic background of sea and sky. Thus horizontal stripes (usually either black and white, or red and white) and other distinctive patterns are displayed on lighthouses around the world. For example, many Canadian lighthouses, including the Head Harbour (East Quoddy) Light, on Campobello Island, New Brunswick, feature red crosses on a white background. Other unusual treatments include the red-and-white diagonal stripes of South Africa's Green Point Light, the black-and-white-diamond motif of North Carolina's Cape Lookout Light, and the black-and-white spirals of Florida's St. Augustine Lighthouse, which give it a marked resemblance to an old-fashioned barber's pole. While white-painted

Below: *A number of Canadian lighthouses, like the Head Harbour (East Quoddy) Light, bear a striking red cross upon their white towers, the bold accent color making the lighthouse stand out distinctly from its natural surroundings.*

towers may be topped by distinctive red lanterns, as seen at the Lindesnes Light in Norway, the superstructures of other lighthouses may be entirely red, like Michigan's Holland Harbor (Black Lake) Lighthouse, which is known affectionately as "Big Red."

Yet the lighthouse is not the only sentinel of the sea: many "lesser aids" of major importance also warn sailors of maritime hazards. These may be either visual—post lights, lightships and buoys, for example—or audible, sounded when weather conditions prohibit good visibility, as in the case of fog signals. In addition, the advent of onboard radio, radar and satellite-navigation systems allows today's mariners to determine their positions from information beamed directly to the bridges of their vessels. This chapter presents an overview of the evolution and workings of these other aids, which, for a variety of reasons, fulfill a live-saving function that the lighthouse itself may be unable to provide.

LIGHTSHIPS

Lightships are particularly suited to offshore locations where unstable foundations would make lighthouse construction a perilous, and ultimately unsuccessful, exercise. The Goodwin Sands, off the coast of Kent in the English Channel, for example, not only present a significant hazard to mariners through their presence, but are constantly shifting, making construction of a stable foundation problematic. Lightships, by contrast, can be relocated easily when necessary. Thus the three lightships now positioned at the eastern, western and southern extremities of the Goodwin Sands help navigators through one of the world's busiest shipping channels. Besides mobility, lightships have other advantages over lighthouses in that they are both comparatively inexpensive to build and easy to maintain. Prior to their automation, the most significant disadvantage was the ongoing cost of a crew at least fifteen strong—and the danger the crew members were exposed to.

In earlier centuries, light vessels were retired seagoing ships, and the first such vessel to assume the official function of a lightship was a sloop (a single-masted, rigged sailing ship) named the *Nore*. Anchored above the Nore Sandbank, at the confluence of the Thames and Medway Rivers in the Thames Estuary on England's eastern coast, from 1732, the *Nore*

Above: *Connecticut's second Stratford Point Lighthouse (1881), a cast-iron conical tower, is predominantly white with a central band of red that renders it unmistakable to mariners sailing toward the Housatonic River.*

alerted sailors to the sandbank's presence by means of candles contained within a pair of lanterns positioned 12 feet (3.7 meters) apart that were suspended from a vertical beam fixed crosswise to the mast. The lanterns were tended by a crew that lived aboard the *Nore*, and, indeed, it would be nearly two centuries before technological progress rendered onboard lightship personnel (sometimes numbering up to twenty people) unnecessary. The *Nore* became the model for five other lightships that were stationed at hazardous points around England's coastline by the end of the eighteenth century. Lightships also served as temporary beacons during the construction of some offshore lighthouses, one, for example, warning navigators off England's Eddystone Rock from 1756 until the third lighthouse here was completed in 1759. Another was stationed off Minots Ledge, Massachusetts, until its second lighthouse was lit in 1860.

Following England's lead, aging vessels were soon pressed into lightship duty all over the world; besides displaying illuminants, they were usually equipped with such fog signals as bells and cannon for use in poor visibility. One of the earliest light vessels in the New World was the former warship *Nuestra Señora de Loreto* (*Our Lady of Loreto*), which guided navigators around Uruguay's Flores Island before the Isla de Flores Lighthouse was raised in 1828. The first U.S. lightship (then called a lifeboat) was positioned in Chesapeake Bay, off Virginia's Willoughby Spit, in 1820, the same year in which Stephen Pleasonton was appointed as fifth Auditor of the Treasury Department. Lightships appealed to Pleasonton's highly developed sense of thrift, and although it became necessary to move the Willoughby Spit Lightship to calmer waters off Craney Island in 1821, many more soon appeared off U.S. shores, including the trail-blazing 230-ton vessel—the first American "outside" lightship—that was stationed in the Atlantic Ocean off Sandy Hook, New Jersey. By 1852, when the Lighthouse Board assumed responsibility for the nation's lights, forty-two crewed lightships were in service.

(continued on page 181)

Below: *Ireland's* South Rock *light vessel docked for servicing in Dún Laoghaire Harbour. A lightship was first stationed at South Rock, off the County Down coast, in 1877; the present vessel, which displays a red light, was automated in 1981.*

CHESAPEAKE

ELEMENTS OF A LIGHTSHIP

Shown on page 173 is the lantern of *Lightship No. 112, Nantucket,* which served on Massachusetts' Nantucket Shoals from 1936 until its decommissioning in 1973. On the outer fold pages is an aerial view of the *Winter Quarter,* which is today moored at Liberty Marina, Liberty State Park, New Jersey.

Launched in 1907, *Lightship No. 87, Ambrose* (shown on page 180) first served as an aid to navigation on the Ambrose Channel, on the southern approach to New York Harbor. It was later reassigned to serve at Staten Island, New York City; Scotland, New Jersey; and Curtis Bay, Baltimore. Retired in 1968, the lightship can today be viewed at New York City's South Street Seaport Museum.

The detail at top shows a lightship's warning bell, which is activated by the vessel's motion, and below is an interior view of the optic in *Nantucket's* lantern room.

MARINA OFFICE
OPEN 7 DAYS
HOURS - 9 to 5

SUN-RUNNER
SEA TRAM

1 *The gimballed masthead light on the* Chesapeake *lightship.*
2 *An elevated fog horn.*
3 *The* Chesapeake's *mushroom anchor, with its heavy-duty chain.*
4 *One of several cleats for the vessel's mooring lines.*
5 *Detail of the mushroom anchor and its safety chain.*
6 *Electrical fog signals.*
7 *Watertight foul-weather hatches for access belowdecks.*

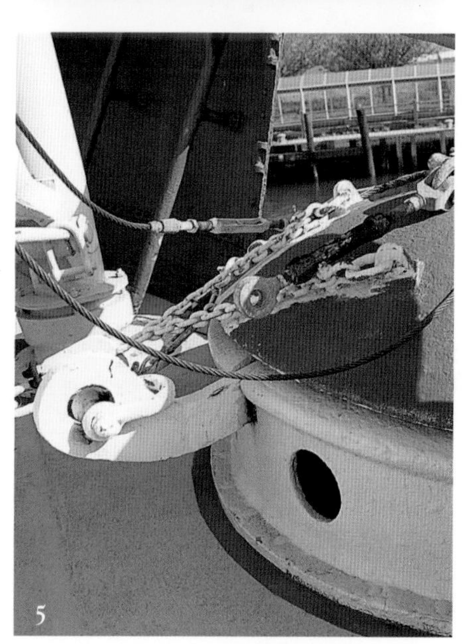

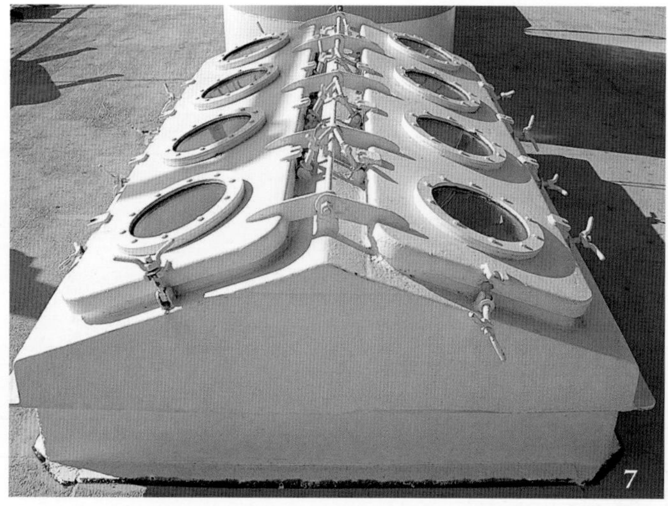

Hard Rock
6
5
4
3
2

AMBROSE

(continued from page 172)

After the U.S. Civil War, during which most light vessels in Southern locations were destroyed, to be replaced by hastily converted tugs, brigs and other vessels, the Lighthouse Board adopted the practice of giving its ships numbers, rather than names. Although U.S. lightships also bore names, these referred to their current stations and were changed when the vessels were assigned to new sites.

In conjunction with advances made by other world lighthouse authorities, the range and effectiveness of the beacons aboard American lightships were improved by the Lighthouse Board through the use of Argand-type lamps and parabolic reflectors. In addition, since the wooden hulls of many lightships had become infested with destructive marine worms, in 1881 the hull of *Lightship No. 43* was constructed around an iron frame that was then clad with pine. A year later, it was decided that future U.S. lightships should be built primarily of iron or steel in preference to wood, although timber continued to be employed until the beginning of the twentieth century.

Despite these improvements, the vulnerability of these mobile light stations to the tremendous force exerted by storm winds and waves remained a matter of concern. Mirroring international attempts to counter the devastating effects of rough seas on light vessels, during the late nineteenth century the hulls of U.S. lightships—which were now being constructed specifically to serve as aids to navigation—became progressively flatter, while the introduction of bilge keels reduced their rolling motion. Other disadvantages of early, wind-powered lightships had included their slow speed and precarious stability: they could not be restationed swiftly without tugboats, nor could they easily withstand storm-force winds. Both problems were addressed in 1891, when *Lightships*

Below: *With its masthead light acting as a beacon in the darkness,* Lightship No. 103, Huron, *attests to its life-saving function from 1921 until 1970. First a relief vessel, it later stood sentry at Gray's Reef, Michigan, and Manitou Shoals, Lake Michigan, before being transferred to Lake Huron's Corsica Shoals in 1935. Today it performs an educational role at Port Huron, Michigan.*

Nos. 55, 56 and *57*, destined for Lake Michigan, became the first such vessels to be fitted with engines. After a series of incidents in which U.S. lightships broke away from their moorings, improved anchoring methods were introduced in 1894. Yet even these sometimes proved ineffective against violent hurricanes, as shown in 1899, when the thick 2-inch (5-centimeter) chain that had tethered *Lightship No. 50* to a mushroom anchor weighing 2 tons (2,268 kilograms) was snapped during a gale. (After a dramatic struggle, her captain managed to beach the vessel with no loss of life.)

Following the introduction of lamps and reflectors, technology for lightship illuminants continued to keep pace with that for lighthouses: *Lightship No. 51*, which was constructed in 1892 and dispatched to Cornfield Point, Connecticut, was the first U.S. vessel to display electrically powered illuminants, which produced a flashing light. As the twentieth century progressed, other technological refinements included the upgrading of onboard fog signals and the introduction of radio beacons and gimbal rings, which allow the light to remain horizontal.

The lightship's future looked increasingly doubtful, however, from the late nineteenth century, when significant numbers were replaced by screwpile and caisson lighthouses and, eventually (from the 1960s), by "Texas towers." Large navigational buoys (LNBs, or, as they are known in Britain, lanbys) finally completed the decommissioning program, and the last active American lightship, *No. 112, Nantucket*, was taken out of service in 1973. However, other nations have retained certain light vessels, those at Goodwin Sands being especially notable for the valuable service that they provide to mariners. Such modern lightships are clearly marked with their names and are often painted bright red to make them more effective daymarks.

POST, HARBOR AND RANGE LIGHTS

Despite the steady development of construction techniques for raising lighthouses at offshore sites, there are some locations at which it is either impossible or impracticable to erect a permanent, solid structure. In such cases, a lightship or buoy may be positioned above, or near, the hazard that mandates an aid to navigation. Lighthouse authorities may also opt for an even simpler solution: a post, or marker, light. Legions of post lights were positioned at strategic points on U.S. inland waterways—primarily on the Mississippi, Missouri and Ohio Rivers—from the 1870s onward. Their placement was prompted by an increase in steamboat traffic and, consequently, in the number of fatalities (an estimated 1,400 between 1825 and 1850) incurred when steamboats hit a submerged obstacle, or failed to negotiate a bend in the river. The sheer number of hazards precluded an expensive full-scale lighthouse-building program; instead, the Lighthouse Board opted for the expedient of post lights. Maintenance costs were modest, even more so because local people were paid to fuel and light them. The first trio of post lights was in operation at Jefferson Barracks, Twin Hollows and Des Peres on the Mississippi by the end of 1874. By 1915 nearly 1,800 had been emplaced along the Mississippi and Ohio Rivers and their tributaries.

Essentially lanterns fixed on poles, U.S. post lights typically comprised wooden or metal posts, sometimes reinforced with bracing or legs, that supported 14-inch (36-centimeter) flat-wicked lamps enclosed in square, or triangular, tin-framed lanterns with glass panes. They were fueled by sufficient quantities of coal oil (kerosene) to last up to eight days. Where the foundations were relatively stable, steps could be attached to the post to give better access to its light; at sites where it was difficult for a post to obtain purchase, river lights were often fixed to trees. Although the majority projected a fixed white beam, occasionally a variant color—usually red—was produced by glazing the lantern with tinted glass. Some installations were made larger by means of winglike, horizontal extensions. Post lights still perform a valuable function on many of the world's great rivers, although they now generally take the form of battery-powered flashing lights set on 20-foot (6-meter) poles.

Broadly similar operational principles underlie many of the minor harbor lights that serve dual purposes: they help mariners to negotiate complex and crowded harbor channels and enable harbor masters to control the volume of shipping entering and leaving their domains. Even where a lighthouse is present, additional lights are required to clarify the route that a vessel should take, and in busy ports, such lights have the advantage of diminutive size, which allows them to be placed where space is extremely limited. Today's directional harbor illuminants display red and green lights, while harbor-traffic-control lights closely resemble those that regulate automobile traffic—vertically stacked illuminants that successively project a red, yellow (or amber) and green beam. In addition, pairs of lights positioned at different elevations and distances—either as components of two light towers or as stand-alone lights on poles—may act as range lights, which, when perceived by the navigator to be in vertical alignment, indicate the safe route. Laser beams are now also used as range lights.

Helpful as such lesser lights may be, they still perform a subsidiary, or supplementary, function to the lighthouse, which projects a more powerful beam. Unlike the lightship, they are unsuitable for exposed locations.

__Below:__ St. Joseph Inner and Outer North Pier Lights were constructed in 1907 as an aid to navigation on Lake Michigan. Their contrasting structures—one conical, the other octagonal—render them unmistakable and, like all range lights, when they appear to be vertically aligned, navigators know that they are steering a safe course.

BUOYS

Like lightships, buoys are classified as floating lights; unlike lightships, however, they appear to have a flourishing future, owing to their efficiency, convenient size, low cost and minimal maintenance requirements. Markers for coastal waters, buoys comprise many different types that have been specially designed to indicate safe channels on the one hand and to warn of obstructions on the other. They also highlight other marine features of special significance to navigators, such as designated mooring places or traffic lanes. The boundaries of the eight channels that were created by dredging the silt that threatened to block Macau Harbor, on an island in the Pearl River estuary in southern China, during the nineteenth century, for example, are all indicated by lighted and unlighted buoys.

Despite historians' uncertainty about exactly when and where buoys were first employed, it is known that the first such aids to navigation in U.S. waters were positioned in the Delaware Bay in 1767. These, as well as their international contemporaries, would have been simple wooden floats attached to ropes that were weighted down to anchor them to the bed of the bay. Over the centuries that followed, wooden, copper-covered buoys and ropes gave way to boiler-iron models (compartmentalized for additional buoyancy) with iron chains. A gas-fueled illuminant was incorporated into a buoy positioned at the approaches to New York Harbor in 1881. To enable the marker to emit an audible signal when obscured by fog, the Lighthouse Board adopted J.M. Courtney's whistling buoy in 1876. Its whistle was activated by the compression of air through the action of the sea. This was supplemented by motion-activated bell buoys in 1885, and the gong buoy made its first appearance in 1923.

During the twentieth century, methods of illuminating buoys progressed from acetylene gas and Sun-valve systems through battery-powered lamps to present-day solar cells. The bulbs are contained within plastic drum lenses and are switched on and off automatically to give them a flashing character. Alternative sources of power may be provided by batteries that are recharged by diesel generators placed aboard the buoy. In the case of some tail-tube buoys, air-turbine generators are powered by the oscillating movement of air and water in the tail tube, as the buoy is tossed upon the sea. Today's LNBs often host fog signals, radio beacons, passive radar-echo enhancers and meteorological instruments, effectively making them well-equipped floating lighthouses.

When they are destined for exposed offshore locations, modern buoys are generally made of steel plate and fitted with steel chains attached to cast-iron or concrete sinkers that anchor them to the sea bed. Those intended for sheltered positions are constructed of lightweight plastic, reinforced with fiberglass, and require less substantial synthetic cables to moor them in position.

***Below:** Numbered buoys provide information to mariners approaching Staten Island, New York. Their positions are marked on local navigation charts and in the U.S. Light List, which details the characteristics and purpose of such floating aids to navigation.*

The stormy conditions to which they are frequently subject, as well as the weight of their heavy chains, mean that offshore buoys must be larger than their inshore counterparts. LNBs may have a diameter of up to 40 feet (12 meters), weigh more than 100 tons (102,000 kilograms) and support a light tower 40 feet (12 meters) high. By contrast, the diameters of inshore floating aids to navigation vary from 3 to 6 feet (1 to 2 meters), and may also take a variety of forms. Tail-tube buoys, for example, whose lights may be positioned at heights ranging from 10 to 20 feet (3 to 6 meters), are also called high-focal-plane buoys, and gain extra stability by means of a central tube submerged beneath the surface. Other variants include spar buoys, which consist of long poles supporting elevated illuminants; conical-topped nun buoys, whose name reflects their resemblance to a nun's headdress; and can buoys—cylinders with flat tops that look like giant food cans. Buoys assume so many forms and colors not only to ensure that they are suited to their sites and readily visible, but also because they transmit specific information by visual means, which can be identified on charts or light lists.

Of course, the language of buoys can be effective only if it is common to, and understood by, all mariners, regardless of nationality. Despite earlier efforts to create an internationally uniform buoyage vocabulary, it was not until 1982 that the International Association of Lighthouse Authorities (I.A.L.A.), galvanized into action by a number of fatalities believed to have been caused by buoyage-related confusion, persuaded fifty countries to conform to the I.A.L.A.'s International Maritime Buoyage System.

By the terms of this system, which is now well established, the globe is divided into Region A (stretching roughly eastward from Europe to Australia) and Region B (extending eastward from the Americas to the Philippines), with broadly similar regulations applying to each region. Buoys are categorized primarily into lateral and cardinal classes, the former marking channels and the latter either a safe passage, or the vicinity's deepest stretch of water. When viewed entering a harbor, lateral buoys include red can buoys displaying a red light that signify a channel's port side in Region A, and its starboard side in Region B, as well as their opposite numbers: conical green buoys that, depending on the region, mark either the channel's starboard or port side. Cardinal buoys are so designated because their black-and-yellow-banded elevated superstructures bear one of four topmarks consisting of cones positioned to emulate the cardinal compass points of north, south, east and west. Yellow buoys bearing a cross-shaped topmark and a yellow illuminant draw mariners' attention to locations that they should avoid, like prohibited sites, while buoys consisting of two globes painted with red-and-black horizontal bands signify a hazard that can be skirted without danger, and vertically banded, red-and-white-striped circular buoys represent a safe area. Since its introduction, there has been little doubt that the I.A.L.A.'s buoyage system has been instrumental in preventing many deaths and vessel collisions.

Above: *According to the I.A.L.A.'s Maritime Buoyage System, when entering a harbor red buoys signal a waterway's port side in Region A and its starboard side in Region B, while green buoys convey the opposite information. Buoys like those pictured here have a partly skeletal structure to make them less wind-resistant and more stable.*

Above: The sun may be shining here on Bass Harbor Head, Ellsworth, Maine, but on the frequent occasions when fog descends upon the coastline the light station's bell is sounded. Sound signals like this help mariners to identify their position when visibility is poor.

SOUND SIGNALS

Until the advent of onboard radio, radar and satellite systems during the twentieth century, fogbound navigators had little choice but to rely on their sense of hearing, and, with luck, the sound of a nearby fog signal, to guide them away from hazards. Although water and wind both distort the quality of sound and mislead the hearer as to the position of its source, an audible signal is better than none at all, and the importance of sound as an aid to navigation, in conjunction with lighthouses, lightships and buoys, has been appreciated for centuries. Indeed, at some coastal locations, fog-signal stations preceded lighthouse construction, as was the case at Point Montara, on California's fog-plagued Pacific coast, off which two major wrecks prompted the installation of a fog signal in 1872. Not until 1900 was a monopole beacon raised at Point Montara, followed by a wooden lighthouse in 1912, and finally a cast-iron light tower in 1928 (although the latter lighthouse is still active, its fog signal has been transferred to an offshore buoy).

Cannon were among the earliest instruments deployed as fog signals, both in Europe and in the New World. Boston Harbor Lighthouse (1716) was the first in North America to be equipped with one, from 1719. They remained in use well into the nineteenth century: Point Bonita Light (1855), for instance, received a 24-pound (11-kilogram) cannon that was manned by an unfortunate former army sergeant who was forced to fire it for three consecutive foggy days and nights soon after he assumed his duties. Another type of sound signal favored in New England from the 1820s was the bell, initially sounded by hand. A mechanical system incorporating a striker that was activated by a rope, or flywheel, attached to falling weights relieved the keeper of this tiring duty later in the century. A clockwork-powered mechanism driven by compressed gas was also introduced, and during the early twentieth century, the combination of electricity and hygroscopes (which monitor the level of humidity in the air) enabled the bell signal to be triggered automatically in foggy conditions.

From the mid-nineteenth century, other ingenious fog-signal devices were developed and experimented with, including gongs, reed trumpets, steam whistles and sirens, all of which produced more powerful signals than bells and could be heard farther out to sea. The steam whistle operated along the same principles as its counterpart for locomotives, being sounded by the steam emitted by a pressurized water boiler, and later by compressed air. It was significantly larger than its railroad variant, however, because it had to project its whistle over far greater distances. The reed trumpet, the invention of C.L. Daboll, was first put on trial by the

U.S. Lighthouse Board at Rhode Island's Beavertail Light in 1851. It was also sounded by compressed air, which caused a reed measuring up to 10 inches (25 centimeters) in length to vibrate; the resultant sound was magnified by an enormous trumpet. It was not until the 1860s that another form of fog signal—the siren trumpet—was introduced to a significant number of U.S. light stations, starting with Sandy Hook's East Beacon Light, New Jersey, in 1868. Fog sirens remained the standard international sound signal for many decades thereafter. Consisting of a rotating perforated-metal drum, the wail that was produced by the passage of compressed air through the perforations was frequently amplified, from the early twentieth century, by a Canadian innovation—the piston-operated diaphone. Another variant was the tyfon, a vibrating-diaphragm horn that was also activated by compressed air.

Almost all of the world's sound signals have now been electrified, and are usually activated by power units that pass an alternating current through an electromagnet, causing a metal diaphragm centered between the electromagnet's poles to vibrate and thus emit a signal that can be heard up to 5 miles (8 kilometers) away. Many lighthouses continue to supplement their beacons with electric foghorns or nautophones, including Poland's Cape Rozewie Light, Ireland's Kish Light, South Africa's Green Point Lighthouse and Croatia's Savudrija Light. Some fog signals, like that at England's South Stack Lighthouse, are stacked vertically to increase the horizontal dispersion of the sound emitted.

Like light beacons, which have individual characteristics, each fog signal has a distinctive sound pattern that is recorded in the International Regulations for Preventing Collisions at Sea, as well as on national light lists and other maritime publications, including the U.S. Notices to Mariners.

Above and left: *The cannon pictured above, stationed at Boston Harbor Light from 1719 until the 1840s, is believed to have served as the United States' first fog signal. In 1872 the same light station instituted the fog horn shown at top, whose sound was amplified by its enormous trumpetlike structure. Modern fog signals, like this siren at Northern Ireland's St. John's Point (left), are significantly smaller.*

Aerobeacons

Advances in technology have contributed greatly to changes in the lighting of lighthouses. Traditional lighthouse evolution came to a halt during the twentieth century for two primary reasons: radio beacons offered longer-range detection, more accurate location, a greater number of fixed points for navigational use, and efficiency both day and night in all weathers; radar offered long-range detection under the control of the navigator, who no longer had to rely on technology beyond his or her command.

Although coastal lighthouses still have a part to play as navigational aids for inshore traffic, it made sense to use a common technology for all navigational demands, and it was thus that the aerobeacon came of age.

Often simple metal lamp enclosures supported on single poles, aerobeacons differ from traditional lighthouses through their wider beam direction and use of radio transmission. The aerobeacon's light sends the same Morse identification codes as the radio beacon. As a result of this shared communicational language, as well as the vertical light beams that are often associated with airport beacons, both air traffic and shipping share common navigational fixed points.

The aerobeacons that are closest to the "old" lighthouse technology use regular light flashes through Fresnel lenses rotating at a constant speed, with the frequency of rotation determining the flash rate to enable the visual-identification signature. The traditional horizontal-flash sequence used by lighthouses has been retained, but with the addition of an explicit Morse-code sequence of low-frequency radio "flashes," thereby enabling the identification of navigational fixed points both visually and instrumentally. Color is also used for identification: for example, the aerobeacon at Wisconsin's La Pointe Lighthouse on Long Island, one of the Apostle Islands in Lake Superior, flashes green.

During the second half of the twentieth century, aerobeacons replaced many lighthouse lenses, either taking their place within the lantern or, as in the case of Kilauea Point Lighthouse in Hawaii, being placed on a monopole outside the lighthouse premises. An unusual example of aerobeacon use can be seen at Piedras Blancas Lighthouse in California, whose lantern was removed entirely, the aerobeacon standing exposed to the elements at the top of the remaining tower, as seen in the aerial photograph of this light station below.

The use of aerobeacons enabled automation, and navigational safety took a giant step forward as aircraft and ships were able to share this new union of technology.

—Jem Smallwood, *Physicist*

RADIO BEACONS, RADAR, SONAR AND RACONS

Above: *A short-range marine radar beacon, or racon, towers above Chile's Punta Delgada Light. Because the information that it transmits is unique, it enables navigators to determine their position accurately.*

Since 1917, when the first radio beacon went into operation, mariners have had access to the invaluable boon of onboard radio-direction finders. After such successful trials as that carried out off England's eastern coast, when the lightship stationed on East Goodwin made contact with North Foreland Lighthouse by means of a wireless set, radio has proved a crucial navigational aid. Radio beacons began to be widely introduced at light stations during the 1920s (the first U.S. installation was at Sea Girt Lighthouse, New Jersey, in 1921), and many remain in operation today. To take advantage of the information that radio beacons transmit, a vessel must be equipped with a radio direction-finder that can receive the radio-beacon's identification signal, which is broadcast in Morse code at a fixed frequency between 285 and 315 kilohertz (the radio beacons at Italy's Livorno and La Lanterna, Genoa, for example, transmit signals on 298.00 and 310.50 kilohertz, respectively). During the minute or so that the radio beacon takes to transmit its encoded signal, it is picked up by the direction-finding receiver. Having received this fix, which is generally accurate to within 3 degrees, navigators can triangulate from aonther point and determine their position, even in dense fog.

Radio beacons fall into the Shoran (short-range navigation) classification of aids to navigation, having a range of only up to 175 miles (282 kilometers). By contrast, long-range navigation (Loran) systems, such as Loran-C, operate over distances of up to 1,242 miles (2,000 kilometers). Loran utilizes a principle similar to that underpinning radar, in that one or two pairs of radio stations (one termed the "master" and the other the "secondary" transmitter), situated at distances of between 621 and 1,242 miles (1,000 and 2,000 kilometers) apart, transmit synchronized pulses to shipboard radio receivers, allowing navigators to work out their positions according to the phase differences in the length of time that it takes each station's signal to arrive.

Radar (radio detecting and ranging) and sonar (sound navigation and ranging) make similar use of radio and sound waves. Radar enables the navigator to obtain positional information by signaling to objects on, and above, the sea's surface, while sonar employs underwater echolocation (determining the position of an object by noting the time that it takes for the object to reflect the echo of a high-frequency sound transmitted to it back to the transmitter, as well as its direction). Although radar was developed during World War II, the first radar beacons (also known as racons, or radar responders) were not introduced for mariners' use until 1966. When the rotating scanner of a ship's onboard radar is directed toward a radar beacon, it sends an interrogation signal that comprises high-frequency radio pulses, which the racon receives and responds to with a coded pulse signal transmitted on a marine radar band of either 9,300 to 9,500 or 2,900 to 3,100 megahertz. This information, which is specific to individual racons, along with the duration of the pulses' return trip and the direction in which they are reflected, allows the shipboard radar to ascertain its host vessel's position. Navigators also use radar to obtain a clearer picture of a nearby coastline, or to identify any offshore hazards that may be invisible to the naked eye. When a radar pulse is transmitted to an object like a buoy, the object similarly reflects the pulse back to the transmitting radar, the time that the retransmission process takes, and direction of the pulse beam, enabling the target object's distance and direction to be measured and hence the position of the navigator's vessel to be established. In order to enhance their reflected signal, buoys are frequently equipped with passive radar-echo enhancers—geometrical metal shapes that capture, and thus return, a greater volume of the radar pulse.

Despite the invaluable service that they provided during the twentieth century, navigators' reliance on all of these high-tech systems is being diminished by such superprecise satellite-navigation systems as the GPS. Indeed, the U.S. Coast Guard has decommissioned all of its radio beacons, although they still survive elsewhere, as do racons, which are still in use at light stations like Ireland's Hook Head and South Africa's Roman Rock.

Below: *Scotland's northernmost light station, Muckle Flugga, on the remote Shetland Islands, is equipped with a short-range ship-to-shore radio beacon fixed atop a monopole that is nearly as tall as the lighthouse.*

SATELLITE-NAVIGATION SYSTEMS AND THE GPS

The swift pace of change in systems of navigation during the second half of the twentieth century can be illustrated by the example of China's Laotieshan Lighthouse, which received a radio beacon in 1959, only to have it superseded in 1997 by a Differential Global Positioning System (DGPS) reference station. Ever since the development of the world's early artificial satellites during the late 1950s, radio transponders stationed on the numerous satellites that now orbit the Earth have been receiving radio signals sent by ground stations and beaming them to receivers in enhanced form. Satellite-navigation systems have culminated in the *NavStar* Global Positioning System, which became fully operational in 1995. The most crucial components of the GPS are twenty-four satellites, set on six orbital paths, which continually transmit radio signals to Earth. Using this system, which is described in detail on the following pages, navigators can now determine their position with an accuracy up to 33 feet (10 meters).

Although it is foreseen that the GPS will soon be improved even further, it is perfectly possible that it, too, will eventually be rendered obsolete by some as yet undreamed of navigation system. Yet whatever the future holds, one thing is certain: people will continue to be fascinated by the tribute to human endeavor represented by more traditional aids to navigation.

Above: *The mast that supports the communication beacon at Nobska Point Light, which is situated at the mouth of Woods Hole Harbor, on Massachusetts' Cape Cod, dwarfs the 40-foot (12.2-meter) lighthouse. Elevating such beacons reduces the risk of interference distorting the signal.*

The Evolution of Navigational Instruments

"Satellite Navigation is the most striking innovation in navigation since the compass for giving orientation, the sextant for determining latitude, and John Harrison's chronometer for determining longitude," said Robert Dietz, when he was at the head of the U.S. National Oceanic and Atmospheric Administration.

Before examining this modern form of navigation in greater depth, it is useful to review briefly the evolution of navigational methods over the ages until their culmination in the Global Positioning System, which remains a source of wonder to many people, even today.

THE EVOLUTION OF NAVIGATIONAL SYSTEMS

People have been navigating in one form or another even before the compass came into existence. The native Australians, for example, managed to find their way around their continent when it was as yet unexplored by Westerners with an accuracy that is still not completely understood, while the earliest seafaring folk, exemplified by the Polynesians, completed extraordinarily long voyages without the aid of what we would define as instruments. The Phoenicians and Vikings, who still astonish us with their feats of navigation, relied on the observation of heavenly bodies, sampling the pattern and direction of the winds, as well as the color and taste of the sea, combined with instinct honed by experience. The ancients' study of astronomy, although mainly for religious purposes, also provided an extensive knowledge of the universe that was put to use by the early navigators. According to Homer, the goddess Athena told Odysseus to "Keep the Great Bear on his left!"

The production of navigational charts, together with the use of a piece of lodestone (a magnetic stone) as a means of indicating the points of what we now call the compass, has been known for more than two thousand years in both the East and West. It is thought that the system of superposing a rectangular grid system (coordinates) on a chart originated in ancient China. According to legend, a lady who was embroidering a map realized the practical use to which the warp and weft of the cloth on which she was working could be put.

The compass has evolved tremendously since those far-off days, greater accuracy being achieved by manufacturing the needle from magnetized steel, floating it in liquid and, when on shipboard, suspending it in gimbals (a suspension device) and placing it in a binnacle (protective housing).

Increasingly detailed and accurate charts and compasses made navigation in those seas where a coastline was never too far away less of a hit-or-miss affair. Bearings could be taken on such recognizable features as headlands and islands, and in this respect lighthouses played a vital part, especially at night and in bad visibility, when their audible fog signals could prevent ships from being wrecked on a hostile coast. A further aid to navigational accuracy was the discovery of a method of measuring a vessel's speed by using an hourglass and a log attached to a knotted cord that was thrown over the side of the ship, enabling the navigator to estimate the distance that the ship was traveling in a certain direction, as well as its speed. Today a ship's speed is still measured in "knots," while a "log" is maintained as a record of progress. A better understanding of the nature of the magnetic pole, and of its predictable changes, also enabled greater accuracy to be achieved.

A notable advance in navigation was the discovery that latitude could be fixed by sighting the Sun, ideally at noon. At first a primitive astrolabe was used for this purpose, then a quadrant, or cross-staff, and later the more refined sextant. By measuring the angle of elevation of the Sun above the horizon, tables could then be consulted to give the latitude, that is, the number of degrees above or below the equator where a ship was positioned. When the Sun was obscured by cloud, a known star—preferably the Pole Star—could be used at night, providing that it was visible. Even in clear weather, however, this method was far from accurate and measurements made from a heaving deck through foam and spray could result in errors of several miles. If no measurements at all could be made for several days, a disaster could result.

At this stage major advances in navigational methods stagnated for centuries. But the discovery of the New World, and its ensuing exploitation by the maritime powers of the day, made an accurate method of fixing longitude imperative. A method of finding longitude on land, which had first been devised by Galileo, was in use for another two centuries. Local time had first to be determined by measuring the position of the Sun or stars, and then the pattern of the movement of Jupiter's four moons. Galileo, who had originally observed these moons through his newly invented telescope in 1610, prepared detailed tables of their movements, by the consultation of which it was possible to compute a position east or west of Galileo's observatory. The invention of a relatively accurate pendulum clock in 1575 made this method far more practicable on land—and replaced the sundial—but a pendulum clock was, of course, of very limited use at sea.

The importance of discovering an accurate means of telling the time precisely during a long sea voyage became so pressing that European monarchs offered extremely large rewards for the successful solution of this problem. John Harrison eventually succeeded with the invention of his chronometer, the first model of which was produced in 1735. There is not enough space in this brief survey to detail the trials and tribulations that Harrison suffered until his chronometer was finally accepted. Readers who wish to delve deeper into this story are advised to consult Dava Sobels's fascinating book, *Longitude*.

It is at this stage that one could claim that the slow evolution of methods of instrument-assisted navigation over the centuries came to a halt. There would be no further great advances until the twentieth century, although many refinements were introduced, such as inertial navigation using gyroscopically controlled compasses. The methodology of terrestrial navigation by instrument remained basically unchanged for hundreds of years.

FROM RADIO WAVES TO SATELLITES

It took World War II to harness the accelerating progress that was being made in science and technology to the service of navigation. Several major, interrelated fields of scientific endeavor and technical progress contributed to a revolution in navigational systems, namely radio, communications, computers and all of the many other disciplines that were associated with the development of satellites.

Following the discovery of radio waves during the early twentieth century, the techniques required to propagate, modulate and receive them rapidly made great strides forward. The frequencies of radio waves cover a wide spectrum, from near the frequency of light to the almost audible. The higher the frequencies, the more directional they become, when they can then be beamed in a way resembling a beam of light. The disadvantage of the higher frequencies, however, is that they cover a relatively small area and cannot travel far through the Earth's atmosphere. Although they can cover a far wider area and travel much farther over the curvature of the Earth's surface, the lower frequencies cannot be made so directional. Extremely high frequencies are normally used to communicate with satellites.

Several ground-based radio-navigation systems, using various frequencies and techniques, were developed during the first half of the twentieth century and were used to guide both ships and aircraft by all of the combatant nations during World War II. Many systems were retained after the war, notably Decca, Loran and Omega; some are still in use for civilian purposes. The disadvantages inherent in the frequencies used, however, are reflected by the limitations of the systems using them.

In 1957 scientists tracking the Soviet Union's *Sputnik* satellite, the first artificial satellite to be placed in orbit around the Earth, first realized the tremendous potential for communications and navigation that satellites could offer. It took only three years for the first communications satellite, *Echo I*, to be launched by the United States in 1960. This reflected radio signals from the Earth back to ground-based receivers. *Telstar*, which was introduced in 1962, could receive radio signals from an Earth-based transmitter, amplify them thousands of times and then retransmit them back to Earth. The disadvantage with *Telstar*, however, was that it could function only when a line-of-sight path existed to both sender and receiver during its orbit. Its successor, *Early Bird* (1965), overcame this problem by being "parked" in such a way that its position was fixed in respect to the rotating Earth below it. Satellite-telephone communications and satellite television were enabled as a result, and, indeed, began to proliferate almost immediately.

During the early 1960s, the U.S. Navy launched a series of military satellites, collectively named *Transit*, providing the first worldwide navigation system. These satellites circled the Earth approximately every 90 minutes, moving in polar orbits about 621 miles (1,000 kilometers) above the Earth. They radiated continuous signals containing information from which a receiver on Earth could calculate its own position with a relatively small (for that time) computer. Thus, for example, a submarine under the polar ice cap could fix its position accurately to within about

525 feet (160 meters), and could then use this information when preparing to launch a ballistic missile. The *Transit* system utilized the Doppler shift effect, whereby the observed frequency (or wavelength) of a signal emitted by a moving body varies in relation to the relative motion between the source and the observer, and this variation can be accurately measured. Many earlier radio-based navigation systems also used the Doppler shift effect, and it still plays a part in some modern systems.

THE GLOBAL POSITIONING SYSTEM

Having progressed through the use of instruments, radio beacons and the early satellite-based systems, aids to navigation have now culminated in the current state-of-the-art system, called the Global Positioning System (GPS). A very simple definition of GPS, published in an educational aid by the U.S. Aerospace Corporation, states: "The GPS system consists of satellites whose paths are monitored by ground stations. Each satellite generates radio signals that allow a receiver to estimate the satellite location and distance between the satellite and receiver. The receiver uses the measurements to calculate where on, or above, the Earth the user is located." The velocity of the receiver's movement can also be calculated. The first two of the *NavStar* series of satellites were launched in 1978, and the launch of the twenty-fifth (stand-by) in 1994 completed the system. Full operational capability was reached on July 17, 1995.

It will make it easier to understand how the system functions if we look in turn at the main elements mentioned in the U.S. Aerospace Corporation's definition, namely, satellites in space, ground stations and user receivers. These elements are known as "segments," consisting of space, control and user segments.

The space segment consists of twenty-four satellites, orbiting in six planes 11,000 nautical miles (20,200 kilometers) above the Earth, each orbit taking twelve hours. They are so positioned that a minimum of four satellites can be simultaneously "seen" from anywhere on Earth. Each satellite is observable for about five hours at a time. Each is equipped with four extremely accurate atomic clocks (accurate to within 3 nanoseconds) and transmits continuously on two separate radio frequencies. These enable a receiver on the ground to know the exact location of each "observed" satellite ("almanac and ephemeris"), as well as the precise time at which the information was transmitted and the time taken between sending and receipt. The ionospheric and tropospheric conditions between satellite and observer are also included, enabling the range of each satellite to be computed, and hence the position of the receiver as well.

The control segment consists of a master control station (MCS) situated at a U.S. Air Force base in Colorado Springs. A monitor station is colocated with it, and four further monitor stations are located around the world at Hawaii, Kwajelein, Diego Garcia and Ascension Island. The monitor stations, except for those at Hawaii and Colorado Springs, are equipped with antennas to enable transmission to the satellites. The monitor stations passively track all GPS satellites in view, collecting data from each. This information is then passed to the MCS, where it is used to assess and estimate the performance of the satellites and their individual clocks. The corrected data is then sent back to the satellites, to be incorporated and retransmitted. The MCS and the monitor stations are in constant communication.

By design, the user segment is the simplest and least sophisticated part of the system. It is geared to "ultrasimplification" for the end user, to the extent that a hand-held receiver may be the size of a modern mobile telephone, although capable of receiving and processing the GPS carrier signals to calculate position, velocity, altitude and time. There is no limit to the number of receivers that can be in use at one time, or to their locations. Users can fix their location to within about 121 feet (37 meters)—and some sources give an accuracy to within 49 feet (15 meters)—and obtain a time accuracy of 180 nanoseconds and a velocity accuracy of 7.8 inches (20 centimeters)

per second. More than 9,000 receivers were used by the Coalition forces during Operation Desert Storm, the hand-held models weighing only 28 ounces (794 grams), which may account for the astonishing accuracy of their cruise missiles, air-borne-weapons systems and artillery.

A good example of the many civil uses to which the system can be put is the construction of the tunnel under the English Channel. The work, which was undertaken simultaneously from both ends, was controlled by GPS receivers, helping to ensure that the two crews met exactly in the middle. There are more than a hundred different receiver models already in use, either hand-held or installed in all manner of vehicles.

The United States Department of Defense provided the GPS primarily for the use of its armed forces and their allies. Up until May 1, 2000, certain essential elements of the information beamed down from the satellites were encrypted (coded) and could be accessed only by authorized users equipped with a receiver capable of converting this data into clear text. Therefore only authorized users could have access to what was called the "Precise Positioning Service" (PPS). The degraded system provided for nonauthorized users was called "Selective Availability" (SA).

However, on May 1, 2000, President Clinton announced that the full GPS system would in future be available to all, enabling civilian users to obtain positioning information ten times more accurate than when SA was in effect. A capability to deny GPS signals on a regional basis when national security was threatened was to be retained. An extract from the press release reads: "Last year...plans [were announced] to modernize GPS by adding two new civilian signals to enhance the civil and commercial service. This initiative is on track and the budget further advances modernization by incorporating some of the new features on up to 18 additional satellites that are already awaiting launch or are in production. We will continue to provide all of these capabilities to worldwide users free of charge."

Differential GPS (DGPS) is a system that enables all GPS users to enhance the performance of their receivers, although extra facilities have to be installed to achieve this. It was originally set up to counter the degradation deliberately introduced into SA signals, and any developments post-May 1, 2000, are awaited with interest. If precise additional information derived from a static, surveyed location can be introduced into a GPS receiver designed to handle it, a much more accurate position can be calculated. This system is based on DGPS sites, which are positioned at exactly surveyed locations. When they receive data from GPS satellites they are thus able to calculate with extreme accuracy any error inherent in a transmission. This error or differential figure can then be broadcast and applied to correct any inaccuracy obtained from the GPS satellites.

Another application of DGPS is determining any timing inaccuracies. These corrections to timing errors can be passed onto the receiver, and can be applied before a positional calculation is made, producing even greater accuracy. Position-only corrections require that the receiver and the DGPS site serving it use the same satellites, and their validity is limited to a range of some 170 miles (274 kilometers) from the site. The sites broadcast by adding an additional modulation to an existing broadcast navigational facility, often Loran-C (as at May 1, 2000), and the user requires an appropriate antenna, receiver and converter box. DGPS is now available in many parts of the world, and the U.S. Coast Guard has already constructed more than forty-eight sites. It is intended that, when complete, the system will provide accuracy to 33 feet (10 meters).

Not only is time correction more accurate than position-only correction, but its corrections can furthermore be broadcast over a much larger area. When correction information is broadcast over a wide area by satellite (not a GPS satellite), this is called Wide Area DGPS (WADGPS). In the United States and Canada, even local radio stations are now transmitting DGPS information on F.M. frequencies.

What of the future? Apart from the ongoing improvements and expansion of existing systems, already given above, no mention has been made here of Soviet and Russian systems. These have, by and large, kept pace with developments in the West. The Russian satellite-based system, *Glonass* (*Gobal'naya Navigatsionnya Sputnikovaya Sistema*), is broadly similar to the American GPS, and it is hoped that some form of integration or interoperability between the two systems may be achieved in the future.

We can, however, be certain that the extremely slow progress in developing navigational systems that we have examined here is very much a feature of the past. The 2000s will see the explosive advance of our ability to navigate with even more safety, although it must fervently be hoped that this acceleration will not be brought about by another major war.

—John Gibson,

Retired British Army Communications Expert

The Continuing Role of the Lighthouse

Despite the relentless march of technology, and the widespread use and efficiency of Long-range navigation (Loran) and the Global Positioning System (GPS), unmanned lighthouses remain active participants in harbor life.

Historic Norwalk, Connecticut, has the distinction of having two such beacons at its harbor channel entrance, the Sheffield Island (pictured above) and Greens Ledge Lights. The former was deactivated in 1902, when cast iron had become a primary building material and caisson foundations enabled construction of the Greens Ledge Light on the mile-long promontory jutting into the entrance to Norwalk Harbor's channel. A third light is located at nearby Pecks Ledge.

Still the most commonly used landmark by boats using the harbor, Greens Ledge can be viewed as a paradigm for the continued use and importance of lighthouses as navigational aids for mariners around the world.

Automated in 1972 with a 190mm optic, the reddish-brown and white beacon is now powered by solar energy, and its alternating red and white signal is still the guiding light for commercial boats, barges and leisure craft. Barry Natale is the new captain of the *Seaport Islander,* also known as the Sheffield Island Ferry, which transports summer tourists from the Hope Dock in South Norwalk to the nearby island in Long Island Sound. According to Captain Natale, "Although the Sheffield lighthouse is inoperative and no longer an active aid to navigation, it is still a charted object, and you can get a bearing on it from a distance. But Greens Ledge is what all the commercial boats use. You keep it on your starboard [right] side and it's the safest way into the harbor."

Motor boats or craft with shallow keels can enter with the lighthouse on their left, or port, side, but must be aware of the sandbar that runs between Greens Ledge and Sheffield Island and is perilous at low tide. Tony Carlo has run his lobster boat, the *Tony C,* out of the Rowayton section of Norwalk for nineteen years. He reports: "I use anything that's fixed, like the lighthouse or buoys, because very often the electronic positioning systems are down." He uses Loran now and will probably switch over to GPS in the near future.

Carlo recalls a fall day when he and his brother, Chris, were out on the Sound when a squall driving 50-miles-per-hour winds and fog came up out of nowhere: "Most fishermen will tell you that the Sound is much more treacherous than the ocean in rough weather," he observes. "The ocean swells, but the Sound chops." The brothers decided to call it a day and headed for home. Chris's boat, the *Lisa Marie,* was faster and should have made it back sooner. But he missed the lighthouse in the storm and ended up at Sheffield Island. Tony, whose radar was being repaired at the time, made it into Norwalk, not because he saw the lighthouse, but because he heard its foghorn.

Richard Petramela is captain of the R.V. *Oceanic*, which conducts oceanography classes, marine-life study tours and winter "creature cruises" for the Norwalk Maritime Aquarium. "For me, the lighthouse is the main reference point for coming in and out of the harbor on all our expeditions," he advises. "It's the primary visual aid out there. I usually rely on Loran or GPS when I'm going somewhere unfamiliar." Jack Schneider, the Aquarium's program director, adds that "We have also run diving trips to the lighthouse and ledge area to replenish the Aquarium's stock. It's a rich area for anemones, sea stars and other fish that dwell in rocky areas."

Petty Officer David Dickinson often patrols Norwalk Harbor in the course of his U.S. Coast Guard duties along the Long Island and Connecticut shorelines. "The lighthouse is the most important marker for us to get in and out of the harbor," he reports. "The GPS and the radar are not always 100 percent accurate. And let's face it, the lighthouse never moves. It's completely reliable." He estimates that during an average summer, five shallow-bottomed pleasure boats will either hit the rocks or get caught on the sandbar near Sheffield Island, so it's much more dangerous for deep-keeled commercial craft, like barges and tugboats.

Marine Officer Robert Studwell, of the Norwalk Police Department, deals with another dozen or so boats that need to be towed in from the reef. The Norwalk Police always have three boats in the water, with two officers on duty off-season and a staff of four during the summer. This does not include the five divers available for evidence recovery, sunken boats and investigating unusual obstructions. "Not so many hit the rocks; more of them run aground," Officer Studwell observes. "It's the people who are not from the area who should use the lighthouse, but don't and get into trouble." With thirty-one years of experience on the force, Studwell cannot recall a single accident involving a commercial craft. He attributes this to the professionalism of licensed sea captains. He's had occasional problems with pleasure boaters who call in false alarms and shoot off flares in the water, but most local boaters are responsible and cautious. Novice pleasure-boater Cathy Dolan of Norwalk has a 17-foot motorboat and doesn't use GPS or Loran. She believes she's better off learning how to navigate using maps. "For me the lighthouse is the center point from which I line myself up, especially at night," she reports. "I have a three-foot draft, so I can come into Norwalk with the lighthouse on my left or right at high tide. But at low tide I don't take any chances. I'm careful to keep it on my right."

Bill Cavanaugh and Dave Hopp, oystermen with Tallmadge Bros. Shellfish on Water Street, remember when the Greens Ledge Lighthouse was manned, back in the mid-1960s. "All lighthouses were built for a reason, and we still use them for the same reasons," says Hopp. "It's a backup and a good one."

Skip Gardella, president of Norwalk Marine Contractors and a co-owner of SoNo Wharf, has been navigating Norwalk Harbor all his life. "The best thing I like about the lighthouse is coming back from Long Island at night. It's the first thing your eye picks up," he notes. "The light from the Pecks Ledge Lighthouse is not as bright." He also mentions what the old-timers refer to as "Old Baldy," a rock that protrudes from the quarter-mile waterway between the Greens Ledge Lighthouse and Sheffield Island, especially hazardous at low tide.

Their obvious functions aside, lighthouses are often awash with fables, fantasy and folklore. Greens Ledge is reputedly named for a pirate who sailed with the legendary Captain Kidd. Allegedly, the citizens of Norwalk left his dead body chained on the rocks to discourage other pirates from pillaging the town. Even the literary references to these beacons has a fixity and firmness that endures. For example, one may compare the following description of an English lighthouse as seen by a child in Virginia Woolf's 1927 novel *To the Lighthouse*, to the appearance of Greens Ledge Light—and many others—today:

"The lighthouse was then a silvery, misty-looking tower with a yellow eye, that opened suddenly, and softly in the evening. James looked at the Lighthouse. He could see the white-washed rocks; the tower, stark and straight; he could see that it was barred with black and white; he could see windows in it."

—Dominic Mariani
Journalist

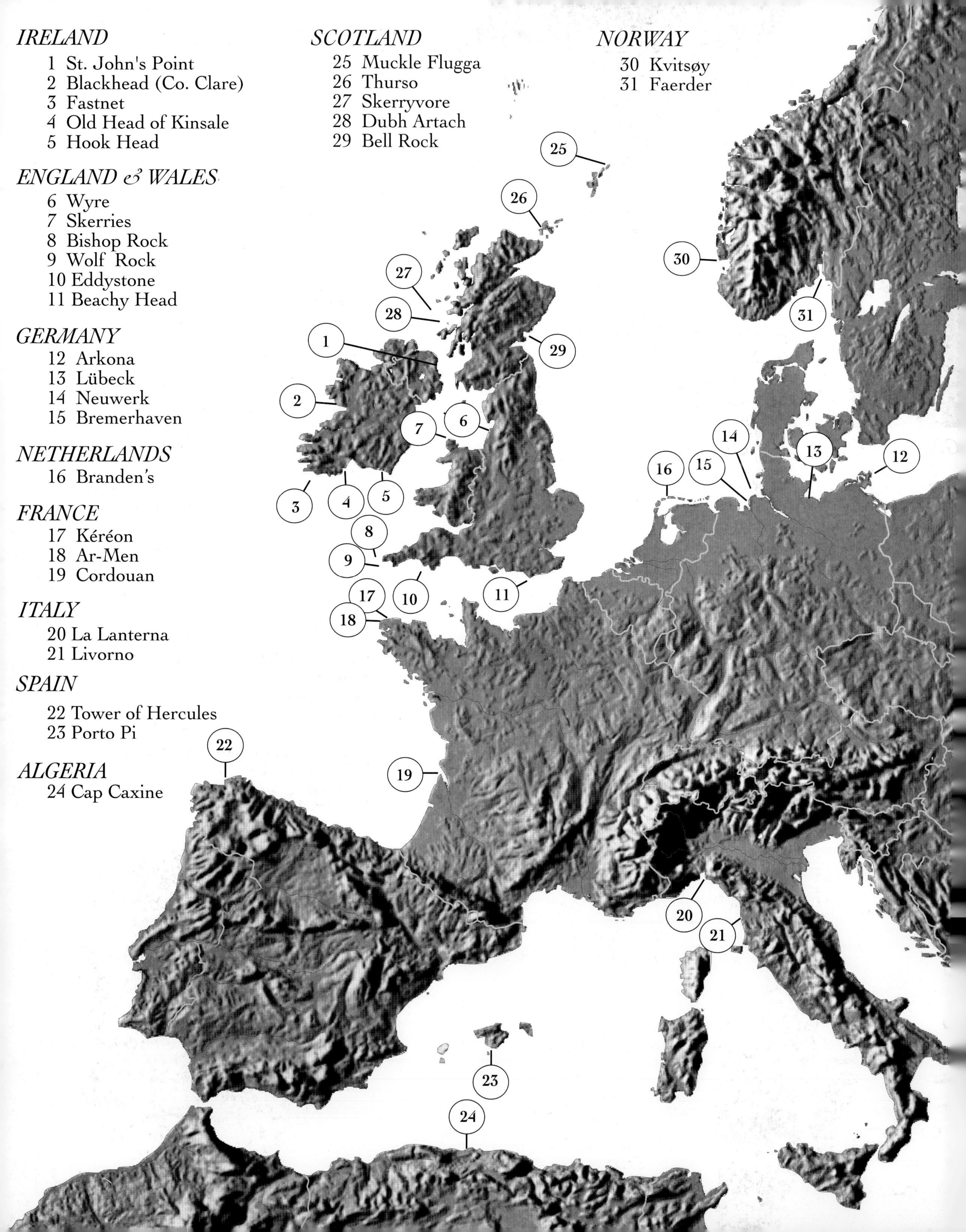
IRELAND
1 St. John's Point
2 Blackhead (Co. Clare)
3 Fastnet
4 Old Head of Kinsale
5 Hook Head
ENGLAND & WALES
6 Wyre
7 Skerries
8 Bishop Rock
9 Wolf Rock
10 Eddystone
11 Beachy Head
GERMANY
12 Arkona
13 Lübeck
14 Neuwerk
15 Bremerhaven
NETHERLANDS
16 Branden's
FRANCE
17 Kéréon
18 Ar-Men
19 Cordouan
ITALY
20 La Lanterna
21 Livorno
SPAIN
22 Tower of Hercules
23 Porto Pi
ALGERIA
24 Cap Caxine
SCOTLAND
25 Muckle Flugga
26 Thurso
27 Skerryvore
28 Dubh Artach
29 Bell Rock
NORWAY
30 Kvitsøy
31 Faerder

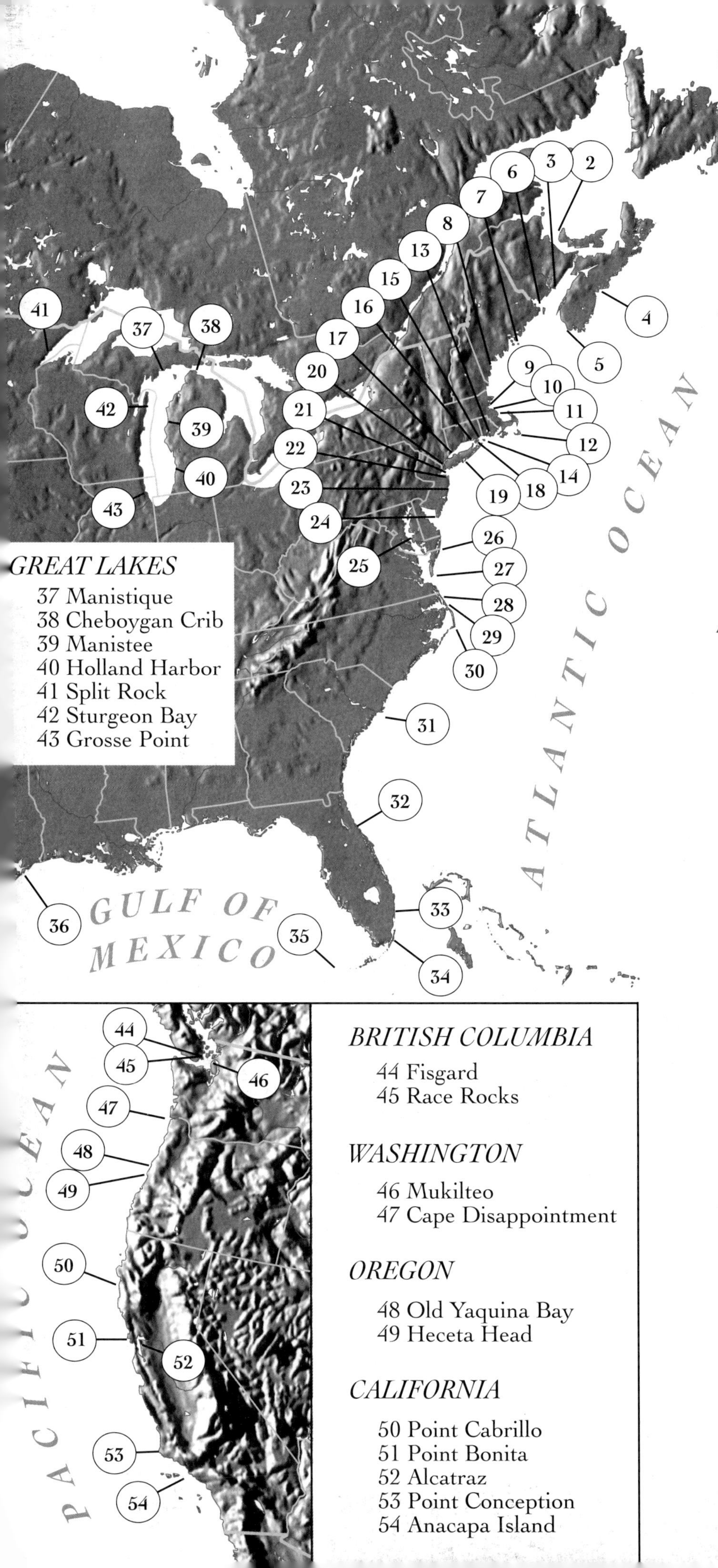

NEWFOUNDLAND

1 Baccalieu Island

PRINCE EDWARD ISLAND

2 West Point

NEW BRUNSWICK

3 St. John Harbor

NOVA SCOTIA

4 Peggy's Cove
5 Cape Forchu

MAINE

5 West Quoddy Hd.
7 Pemaquid Point
8 Portland Head

MASSACHUSETTS

9 Boston Harbor
10 Minots Ledge
11 Graves Ledge
12 Nantucket Island

RHODE ISLAND

13 Castle Hill
14 Block Island

CONNECTICUT

15 Mystic Seaport
16 New London Ledge
17 Greens Ledge

NEW YORK

18 Race Rock
19 Fire Island
20 Statue of Liberty

NEW JERSEY

21 Sandy Hook
22 Highlands
23 Barnegat
24 Cape May

MARYLAND

25 Thomas Pt. Shoal

VIRGINIA

26 Assateague Island
27 Cape Henry

NORTH CAROLINA

28 Currituck Beach
29 Bodie Island
30 Cape Hatteras

SOUTH CAROLINA

31 Cape Romain

FLORIDA

32 Ponce de Leon Inlet
33 Hillsboro Inlet
34 Fowey Rocks
35 Dry Tortugas

TEXAS

36 Bolivar

GLOSSARY

Words in **boldface** *refer to separate entries.*

Abrasion: the wearing away of a surface by the action of fragments of rock. *See also* **attrition, corrasion** and **erosion.**

Accretion: the process by which a shoreline is increased, often by **deposition.**

Acetone: a liquid solvent in which **acetylene** gas may be liquefied.

Acetylene: also known as ethylene or ethene, a flammable, soluble gas that can be used to fuel an **illuminant** when dissolved in **acetone.** *See also* **Agamassan.**

Advection fog: fog caused by the collision of either warm air with a cooler, moist surface, or of warm and cool air currents, the resultant condensation producing water vapor and hence fog. *See also* **radiation fog.**

Aerobeacon: an **illuminant** comprising an open-ended cylinder from which light is beamed in **Morse-code** flashes.

Agamassan: a substance that absorbs **acetylene** gas, invented by Nils Gustaf Dalén (1869–1937).

Air-turbine generator: a device within the tail of a **tail-tube buoy** that converts the kinetic energy of oscillating air and water into mechanical energy. *See also* **generator.**

Aluminum: a metallic element that is light and malleable.

Argand lamp: an oil-fueled lamp invented by Aimé Argand consisting of a coiled **wick** and glass chimney.

Ashlar: either a square block of stone cut for building purposes, or a thin piece of dressed stone used for facing walls.

Attrition: the wearing away of a surface by friction. *See also* **abrasion, corrasion** and **erosion.**

Automation: in lighthouse terminology, the operation of the lighthouse's functions by automatic rather than manual means.

Backwash: the washing back of sea water caused by the action of waves. *See also* **swash.**

Ballast: a heavy material, such as rock, that is used to weigh down and stabilize a vessel or structure.

Bar: an **offshore** ridge consisting of mud, sand, or **shingle** that extends across, or bars, the entrance to, or mouth of, a river, harbor, or bay.

Barrier: an **offshore** feature, such as a **sandbank, sandbar**, island, **shoal**, or **reef** that presents a barrier to mariners nearing the coast.

Beach light: a lighthouse constructed on a beach.

Beacon: a light (and also a radio or **radar**) signal, such as that projected by a lighthouse.

Beaufort Scale: the scale by which the velocity of wind is measured, ranging from 0 (calm) to 12 or, in the U.S.A., 17 (hurricane). Named after its inventor, Sir Francis Beaufort (1774–1857).

Bedrock: foundation rock.

Bilge keel: a form of keel at the lower part of a ship's hull where the sides curve and taper inward toward the bottom.

Biological weathering: the erosion of a rock surface by rock-boring mollusks. *See also* **solution.**

Boiler iron: also known as boiler plate, a tough form of steel from which **buoys** may be constructed for permanent placement as channel markers etc.

Breakwater: a manmade wall projecting into the sea that protects a harbor or shore from the action of the waves. *See also* **groin, mole, pier** and **spur.**

Buoy: a clearly visible floating object, sometimes supporting an **illuminant** and **fog signal**, that is anchored to the sea bed and designates both marine hazards and safe passages. *See also* **can buoy, cardinal buoy, floating light, high-focal-plane buoy, large navigational buoy, lateral buoy, nun buoy, spar buoy** and **tail-tube buoy.**

Buoyancy: the ability to float on water.

Caisson: a watertight structure, open at both ends, that enables water to be drained from an **offshore** site and may subsequently be filled with rocks or concrete to provide a submarine lighthouse foundation. *See also* **cofferdam, crib** and **pneumatic caisson.**

Can buoy: a form of **buoy** that comprises a cylinder with a flat top.

Candela: a unit of measurement of the **luminous intensity** of an **illuminant**, once known as candlepower, from the strength of a candle's light.

Cantilever: a structural component that is fixed only at one end, the other projecting into space.

Capstan: a device with a rotating drum used either for drilling or hauling in.

Carbon arc lamp: a lamp comprising an electric arc between two carbon electrodes.

Cardinal buoy: a **buoy** that indicates a safe passage, or water of the greatest depth in a given vicinity. *See also* **lateral buoy.**

Cast iron: iron containing high levels of carbon that is cast into molds when molten.

Catoptric: a lighting system in which the **illuminant** is placed in front of a **parabolic reflector.** *See also* **dioptric.**

Cavitation: the widening of fissures in a rock that eventually causes it to collapse. *See also* **hydraulic shock.**

Cement: a mixture of clay and **limestone** that is combined with water and sand to create a building mortar. *See also* **concrete** and **hydraulic mortar.**

Chalk: a soft, white, **sedimentary rock** consisting of calcium carbonate. *See also* **limestone** and **solution.**

Character: with reference to lighthouse illumination, the distinguishing quality of an **illuminant,** such as its color and/or the pattern of its flashes.

Coalescence: the fusion of numerous small particles to form a single mass, as occurs when frozen water crystals fuse to form ice.

Coastal geology: the study of the character of a coastline.

Cofferdam: also known as a coffer, a watertight structure that enables sea water to be removed and the foundations prepared for a lighthouse at an **offshore** site. *See also* **caisson, crib** and **pneumatic caisson.**

Colza oil: oil obtained from rapeseed, once used as a fuel for **illuminants.**

Compressed air: air that is compressed to a higher pressure than the air in the atmosphere, used to power a device like a **fog signal.**

Concrete: a durable building material mixed from sand, stone, **cement** and water that is initially liquid but hardens when exposed to air. *See also* **prestressed concrete** and **reinforced concrete.**

Coral reef: a **reef** made up of corals that have aggregated into **limestone.** *See also* **fringing reef.**

Corrasion: the wearing away of a surface by fragments of rock carried by water, wind and ice. *See also* **abrasion, attrition** and **erosion.**

Crib: also known as a crib dam, a supportive framework of timber beams that may be filled with **ballast** to form the underwater foundation of an **offshore** lighthouse. *See also* **caisson, cofferdam** and **pneumatic caisson.**

Cribbage: *see* **grillage.**

Crossbracing: supplementary braces (beams or rods) laid in a crosswise pattern to support and reinforce a structure.

Cumulonimbus clouds: vertically shaped clouds that are dark at the bottom and herald rain.

Cyclone: the name given to a **tropical cyclone** in the Bay of Bengal.

Daymark: an object, such as a lighthouse, that is clearly visible during the day.

Delta: *see* **estuary.**

Deposition: the depositing of **erosional** debris on a coastline by the sea or wind. *See also* **accretion** and **longshore drift.**

Diaphone: a **fog signal** that is operated with pistons.

Differential Global Positioning System (DGPS) station: a station that transmits additional information to a **Global Positioning System** receiver, thereby enabling greater positional accuracy to be obtained.

Dioptric: a lighting system whereby the lens is placed in front of the **illuminant.** *See also* **catoptric.**

Dovetailing: a constructional technique whereby a wedge-shaped tenon, or peg, of wood or stone is inserted in a mortise, or slot, in another to achieve a close fit.

Dressed stone: stone whose surface has been prefinished.

Drum lens: a rotating lens system whose shape resembles that of a drum.

Electromagnet: a magnet that contains a wire-wound iron or steel core through which an electric current is passed.

Electromagnetic induction: the production of electromotive force by means of a bar magnet and a coil of wire.

Elevation: in lighthouse terminology, the height of an **illuminant** above sea level.

Erosion: the wearing away of the coastline by the action of the sea, wind and ice. *See also* **abrasion, attrition, corrasion, deposition** and **longshore drift.**

Estuary: the widening of a river mouth as it approaches a sea or a lake, also known as a delta where there are tributaries.

Fetch: the distance that the wind can travel unimpeded over a body of water.

Fiberglass: a weblike material made of slender glass fibers.

Flange: either a rim that projects from, or around, an object, or a bladelike extension.

Floating light: an **illuminant**-supporting object that floats on the water, such as a **buoy** or **lightship.**

Flotsam: floating wreckage. *See also* **jetsam.**

Flying buttress: a supporting buttress, or **pier,** that extends outward and downward from a structure.

Focal distance: or focal length, the distance between the **focal point** of a lens and the center of the lens, where the **illuminant** may be placed. *See also* **Fresnel lens** and **orders.**

Focal plane: a perpendicular plane that passes through the **focal point** of a lens.

Focal point: the point on a lens upon which parallel rays of light converge, or diverge, following their reflection or **refraction.**

Fog: *see* **advection fog** and **radiation fog.**

Fog signal: an audible signal that gives mariners a means of orienting themselves in fog. Cannons, bells, whistles, gongs, reed trumpets, sirens, **diaphones** and **tyfons** have all been used as fog signals or nautophones.

Fog-signal-emitter stack: a number of vertically stacked **fog signals** or nautophones.

Frazil ice: frozen sea water.

Fresnel lens: the lens invented by Augustin-Jean Fresnel (1788–1827), which consists of concentric ridges radiating outward from the central lens, with prisms positioned at the top and bottom of the ridges to **refract** the light from an **illuminant** placed behind the central lens. The lenses are grouped into various **orders.**

Fringing reef: a **coral reef** attached to the shore.

Gale: a wind measuring 8 on the **Beaufort Scale**, traveling at 34 to 40 **knots**.

Gallery: part of the lighthouse's **superstructure**, a railed walkway that surrounds the exterior of the lantern room.

Generator: a machine, usually powered by diesel oil, that generates electricity; some generators can harness the power of the wind. *See also* **air-turbine generator**.

Geomorphology: the study of the surface of the Earth's crust.

Gimbal ring: also known as gimbals, two or three rings positioned at right angles to each other that hold a compass or other instrument in free suspension.

Global Positioning System (GPS): a system by which twenty-four **satellites** orbiting the Earth on six paths transmit radio signals to receivers, enabling positional information to be obtained. *See also* **Differential Global Positioning System.**

Granite: a hard, **igneous rock** made up of feldspars and quartzes (both crystalline minerals).

Grillage: a supportive foundation for a lighthouse that is constructed of a crosswise arrangement of beams. Also called a **cribbage**.

Groin/groyne: a manmade barrier projecting from the shore that controls **erosion**. *See also* **breakwater, mole** and **spur**.

Headland: a strip of land that extends into the sea or lake. *See also* **promontory**.

Helicoidal: having a spiral shape.

Helipad: a landing site for helicopters, often constructed on, or adjacent to, an isolated lighthouse.

High-focal-plane buoy: a **buoy**, such as a **spar buoy** or **tail-tube buoy**, which supports an elevated **illuminant**.

Hurricane: a wind measuring 12 on the **Beaufort Scale**, traveling at more than 63 **knots**. The U.S. terminology for a **tropical cyclone**.

Hydraulic mortar: mortar consisting of **limestone** and/or **cement** which, when mixed with water and sand, hardens underwater.

Hydraulic pressure: pressure exerted by the action of water.

Hydraulic shock: the process by which the pressure of compressed water or air at the front of a wave causes the degeneration of a hard surface, such as rock. *See also* **cavitation.**

Hygroscope: a device that indicates the air's humidity level.

Igneous rock: rock that was originally lava or **magma** that cooled and solidified beneath, or on the surface of, the Earth. *See also* **granite.**

Illuminant: a light-generating device.

Incandescent mantle: a mantle of metal mesh shaped into a dome or cylinder form that becomes incandescent when heated by a burning fuel, such as **kerosene**. *See also* **incandescent oil-vapor lamp.**

Incandescent oil-vapor lamp or burner: a lamp whose light is generated by pressurizing **kerosene** or petroleum, mixing it with air in a vaporizer chamber, and burning it under an **incandescent mantle**.

Inshore: situated in the sea, close to the shore. *See also* **offshore.**

Inside: another word for **inshore.** *See also* **outside.**

Isophase light: the **character** of a light in which its flash and eclipse are of equal durations. *See also* **occulting light.**

Jetsam: cargo or **ballast** thrown overboard to lighten a vessel during an emergency. *See also* **flotsam.**

Kerosene: another name for **mineral oil.**

Knot: another name for **nautical mile.**

Landfall: the land that a mariner first sights when nearing the coastline.

Lantern: a structure at the top of a light tower that contains the **illuminant** and is usually glazed.

Large navigational buoy (LNB): also known as a lanby in Britain, a large **buoy** that is often positioned at a significant distance **offshore.**

Lateral buoy: a **buoy** that marks a channel. *See also* **cardinal buoy.**

Lever light: also known as a *vippefyr*, an **illuminant** that is suspended from a lever that enables it to be raised or lowered.

Light: either the **illuminant** itself or a lighthouse.

Light list: a list of the aids to navigation maintained by a maritime nation.

Lightship: a vessel that acts as a lighthouse, being equipped with an **illuminant** and **fog signal,** that is moored at an **offshore** location. *See also* **floating light.**

Limestone: a calcium-carbonate-containing **sedimentary rock.** *See also* **cement, chalk, coral reef** and **solution.**

Longshore currents: water currents that move parallel or oblique to the shore. *See also* **longshore drift.**

Longshore drift: the process by which **longshore currents** cause **erosion** and **deposition** by carrying beach debris laterally along the shore.

Loom: the halo effect created above an **illuminant** when water vapor in the atmosphere diffuses the light upward.

Loran: short for long-range navigation, radio aids to navigation that have a longer range than **shoran** aids. The loran system comprises two pairs of radio stations that transmit synchronized radio pulses to an onboard radio receiver, the differences in the signals transmitted by each enabling positional information to be obtained.

Luminous intensity: the strength of the light that an **illuminant** radiates in a specific direction, measured in **candelas.**

Luminous range: the distance that an **illuminant** projects its beam.

Magma: molten rock. *See also* **igneous rock.**

Masonry: stone- or brickwork.

Mercury: also known as quicksilver, a liquid metallic element.

Metamorphic rock: rock whose character has been changed through the action of pressure and heat.

Meteorology: the study of the Earth's atmosphere and the formation of weather types.

Mineral oil: also known as **kerosene** or **paraffin**, once used to fuel **illuminants.**

Mole: another name for a **breakwater.** *See also* **groin** and **spur.**

Monopole: a supportive structure for an **illuminant** consisting of a single pole. *See also* **post light.**

Morse code: the telegraphic language invented by Samuel Finley Breese Morse (1791–1872) that consists of audible dot-and-dash signals.

Nautical mile: or knot, a unit of measurement equaling 1.85 kilometers (1.15 statute miles) used to measure the speed of seagoing vessels.

Nun buoy: a form of **buoy** that has a conical top.

Occulting light: an **illuminant** that is switched off at regular intervals to give its light a specific **character.** *See also* **isophase light.**

Oceanography: the study of the ocean.

Offshore: situated at sea, a significant distance from the shore. *See also* **inshore.**

Orders: the seven classes into which **Fresnel lenses** with different **focal distances** are divided: one through six, plus a three-and-a-half-order lens.

Outside: another word for **offshore.** *See also* **inside.**

Parabolic reflector: a **reflector** that has a paraboloid, or conic-section, shape.

Paraffin: another name for **mineral oil.**

Passive radar-echo enhancer: a geometrical, metal extension to a **buoy** that enhances the **radar** signal that is reflected to a transmitter.

Pharos: the world's first dedicated lighthouse, which stood on the island of Pharos from about 280 BC until its destruction in 1346, guiding ships into the Egyptian port of Alexandria. The French and Spanish names for lighthouses are derived from the Pharos.

Pier: a manmade structure with a deck that extends over
the water, or a load-bearing pillar. *See also* **breakwater** and **flying buttress.**

Pile: also known as a straightpile, a long, straight post made of timber, iron, steel, or concrete which is driven into the sea bed or ground to provide a supportive foundation for a lighthouse. *See also* **screwpile** and **stanchion.**

Pneumatic caisson: a boxlike **caisson,** open at one side, that enables work to be carried out underwater and may later be filled with **ballast** to provide an underwater lighthouse foundation. *See also* **cofferdam** and **crib.**

Portland stone: stone quarried from the British Isle of Portland that is renowned for its excellent constructional properties.

Post light: an **illuminant** set atop a post, often used as a marker **beacon** on rivers. *See also* **monopole.**

Prestressed concrete: concrete in which stretched steel wires are embedded. Used in lighthouse construction to help the structure resist destruction by earthquakes. *See also* **reinforced concrete** and **tensile strength.**

Promontory: an elevated section of land that extends into the sea. *See also* **headland.**

Purchase: a firm hold.

Racon: short for **radar** beacon and also known as a radar responder, a fixed station that transmits a pulse signal containing coded information by radar in response to a signal from a vessel, thereby enabling positional information to be obtained.

Radar: short for radio detecting and ranging, the process by which radio pulses are transmitted to an on- or above-surface object, the direction and duration of the reflected signal
enabling positional information to be obtained. *See also* **sonar.**

Radiation fog: fog caused by the swift cooling of heat in the atmosphere. *See also* **advection fog.**

Radio beacon: a fixed station that transmits a unique radio signal in **Morse code** to a vessel's **radio-direction finder,** thereby enabling mariners to orientate themselves.

Radio-direction finder: an onboard device which receives a **radio beacon's** identification signal.

Range light: one of two **illuminants,** or lighthouses, whose lights indicate a safe passage when in vertical alignment.

Reef: a rocky or sandy ridge submerged beneath the surface of the sea that may be exposed at low tide. *See also* **barrier, sandbar** and **shoal.**

Reflector: an object comprising a mirror, or polished metal surface, that reflects light. *See also* **parabolic reflector.**

Refraction: the bending of the direction of a light beam. *See also* **focal point.**

Reinforced concrete: concrete into which steel rods or mesh have been embedded to give it **tensile strength.** *See also* **prestressed concrete.**

Rivet: to secure with a metal pin, also known as a rivet.

Rubblestone: pieces of broken rock, stone, or brick.

Sandbank: a bank of sand on the sea bed that may be exposed at low tide. *See also* **barrier, reef** and **shoal.**

Sandbar: a ridge of sand on the sea bed that may be exposed at low tide. *See also* **barrier.**

Sandstone: a **sedimentary rock** comprising particles of sand and various minerals.

Satellite: in the lighthouse context, an artificial device that orbits the Earth receiving and transmitting radio signals. *See also* **Global Positioning System.**

Screwpile: a **pile** with a **helicoidal flange** at one end that enables the pile to be screwed securely into the **substratum.**

Sediment: particles of mineral or organic matter that are deposited by water, wind, or ice.

Sedimentary rock: rock formed by the **coalescence** of mineral or organic debris following their movement by wind, water, or ice. *See also* **limestone** and **sandstone.**

Shifting sands: sands that are shifted to different positions by the action of the sea and air.

Shingle: gravel produced by the breaking down of beach pebbles through the action of the sea.

Shoal: a submerged rocky platform or **sandbank** that may be exposed at low tide. *See also* **barrier** and **reef.**

Shoran: acronym for short-range navigation, radio and radar aids to navigation whose range is shorter than **loran** aids.

Silt: deposits of mud or clay on a lake or river bed.

Sinker: a weight attached to a chain or rope that causes it to sink in water.

Skeletal/skeleton tower: an iron or steel tower whose components have been pared down to the bare essentials.

Skirt keel: a circular keel that gives a **buoy** additional stability.

Solar cell: a cell that converts sunlight into electricity.

Solution: the weathering, or **erosion,** of the surface of **chalk** or **limestone** rock by water, air, or rain. *See also* **biological weathering.**

Solventil: a Sun-responsive device invented by Nils Gustaf Dalén (1869–1937) that automatically turns an **illuminant** on at night and off during the day.

Sonar: short for sound navigation and ranging, a system that enables positional information to be obtained by the transmission of a radio signal to a submerged object and the noting of the direction and duration of the reflected echo. *See also* **radar.**

Spar buoy: a **buoy** that comprises a pole supporting an elevated **light.** *See also* **high-focal-plane buoy.**

Spermaceti oil: oil obtained from the heads of sperm whales, once used as a fuel for **illuminants.**

Spider lamp: an **illuminant** comprising a pan of oil containing up to ten **wicks.**

Spit: a strip of **shingle** or sand that extends from the shore into the sea.

Spur: another name for a **groin.** *See also* **breakwater** and **mole.**

Stanchion: a supportive pole. *See also* **pile.**

Storm: a wind measuring 10 to 11 on the **Beaufort Scale,** traveling at a rate of 55 to 63 **knots,** often accompanied by rain, hail, thunder and lightning.

Storm surge: a dramatic increase in the size and swell of waves caused by **storm** winds, rain and high tides.

Straightpile: another word for **pile.**

Subsidence: the process by which a structure slowly sinks.

Substratum: a layer of rock, clay, sand, or mud, beneath the ground's surface, which may serve as the foundation upon which a lighthouse is built.

Superstructure: the main body of the lighthouse that rises above its foundations.

Swash: the dashing action of waves upon a shoreline. *See also* **backwash.**

Tail-tube buoy: a **buoy** with a stabilizing tube attached to the bottom. *See also* **high-focal-plane buoy.**

Tallow: a substance extracted from animal fat that is used to make candles.

Tensile strength: the ability to withstand longitudinal tension or stress. *See also* **prestressed concrete** and **reinforced concrete.**

"Texas tower": an **offshore, pile-**foundation lighthouse that resembles an oil rig.

Tidal wave: an exceptionally high wave that travels in the direction of the shore; a wave generated by the tide.

Topmark: a mark on the top of a **buoy** that signals specific information.

Tripoli powder: the powder obtained when silica-containing rock is ground down; used as a polish.

Tropical cyclone: spiraling, swiftly moving, westward-traveling winds that arise over the sea. *See also* **cyclone, hurricane** and **typhoon.**

Tsunami: an exceptionally large sea-surface wave caused by seismic or volcanic activity on the sea bed.

Tyfon: a **fog signal** consisting of a horn and a vibrating diaphragm.

Typhoon: the name given to a **tropical cyclone** in Pacific Ocean countries.

Waterspout: columns of sea water created and transported by circulating winds.

Westerlies: the prevailing, westward-blowing winds of temperate latitudes.

Wick: a fibrous cord within a candle or oil lamp that, when lit, burns to produce a light.

Xenon: a gaseous element that may be used to produce a bright **illuminant.**

ABOUT THE CONTRIBUTORS

John Gibson was commissioned from the Royal Military Academy Sandhurst into the British Army's Royal Corps of Signals and received his technical education at what is now the Royal School of Signals. He is a graduate of the German Command and General Staff College (*Führungsakademie der Bundeswehr*), where he was later an instructor. He has served in the Royal Signals and the Queen's Gurkha Signals in Singapore, Malaysia, Borneo, Nepal, The Netherlands and Germany, mainly with the British Army of the Rhine. He has experience at the headquarters of every level of military command, from brigade to army, and has served on the communications and electronics (C. and E.) staffs of two N.A.T.O. headquarters: Northern Army Group and Allied Forces Central Europe. He was also the director of a national command-and-control project in the British Ministry of Defence and the controller of its Defence Operations Centre during the Falklands conflict.

J. Keith Hunt is a consultant architect and town planner based in Lytham St. Annes, Lanchashire, England—a few miles south of the site of the Wyre Light, Fleetwood. He has more than thirty years' experience of both residential and public building projects in the region and a keen interest in local history.

James Hyland is a native of Toledo, Ohio, and graduated from Purdue University. He earned a Master of Divinity degree at Gordon-Conwell Theological Seminary in Hamilton, Massachusetts. He serves as president and founder of The Lighthouse Preservation Society, the nonprofit organization that has made lighthouse preservation a national issue with Congressional hearings, conferences, the sponsorship of National Lighthouse Day and its celebrations, the nomination of ten U.S. lighthouse stamps, and the raising of nearly $6 million for more than 160 lighthouse projects. The dedicated group is the recipient of a Presidential Achievement Award for its efforts to preserve our lighthouse heritage.

Heinz Lindenberg was born and brought up in Hamburg. His special interest is Hamburg's history, and as a keen sailor he has a mariner's appreciation of Hamburg's relationship with its neighboring coastal regions. He is also dedicated to ensuring that the Low German dialect spoken in this area is kept alive.

Dominic Mariani has been a foreign correspondent for Universal Press Syndicate based in Rome for three years. He has taught composition and media at Fairfield University, the University of Bridgeport and Norwalk Community College. He is currently an editor with the *Westport News* and writes and edits for many local and national magazines as well the Connecticut Weekly section of the Sunday *New York Times*.

Glenn O. Myers is a consultant in international telecommunications engineering who has participated in a wide variety of engineering projects on four continents and under three oceans plus several seas.

Jem Smallwood, originally a biologist, taught high-school physics for a number of years in the English county of Kent. His sailing experiences in the English Channel and the Dover Straits, one of the world's busiest sea lanes, as well as in French coastal waters, has promoted his interest in safety issues for inshore sailors. He lives within sight of North Foreland lighthouse, at the south-eastern extremity of England, which was until recently the British Isles' last manned beacon.

Robin Langley Sommer is a writer and editor whose published works include fourteen books on American and international architectural history. She is a resident of Greenwich, Connecticut, and has a special interest in lighthouses.

Tom Tasselmyer, meteorologist and author of the feature on hurricanes, is a native of Baltimore, Maryland, and was educated at North Carolina State University. He has held the position of meteorologist at television stations WVVA-TV in Bluefield, West Virginia; WEWS-TV, Cleveland, Ohio; and WBAL-TV/RADIO, Baltimore, where he is now Chief Meteorologist. Married, with four sons, he makes his home in Maryland.

BIBLIOGRAPHY & SOURCES

Baedeker, K., *Hamburg und die Niederelbe*, Verlag K. Baedeker, Hamburg, 1951.

Bathurst, Bella, *The Lighthouse Stevensons*, HarperCollins Publishers, London, 1999.

Beaver, Patrick, *A History of Lighthouses*, The Citadel Press, Secaucus, New Jersey, 1973.

Benchley, Peter, and Judith Gradwohl, *Ocean Planet: Writings and Image of the Sea*, Harry N. Abrams, New York, with the Smithsonian Institution, 1995.

Briggs, David, and Peter Smithson, et al., *Fundamentals of the Physical Environment*, Routledge, London, 1997.

Burroughs, William J., et al., *The Nature Company Guides: Weather.* Time-Life Books, New York, 1996.

Cederberg, Goran, Ebbe Almquist, et al., *Lighthouses of the World: A History of Where Land Meets Sea*, Chartwell Books, New York, 1990.

Comfort, Judith, *Rediscover the Lighthouse Route: A Personal Guide to the South Shore of Nova Scotia*, Nimbus Publishing, Halifax, Nova Scotia, 1995.

Crane Hill Publishers, Pinpoint Guide series American Lighthouses: California; Eastern Great Lakes; Western Great Lakes; Mid-Atlantic; South Atlantic, 1998.

Crompton, Samuel W., and Michael J. Rhein, *The Ultimate Book of Lighthouses*, Saraband Inc., Rowayton, Conn., 2000.

Curtis, Bill, *The Lighthouses of Fleetwood: A Brief History*, (n.p.), 1993.

Demillo, Rob, *How Weather Works.* Ziff Davis Press, New York, 1994.

Denham, Capt. Henry Mangly, R.N., *Description of Wyre Lighthouse, Fleetwood, England*, n.d.

Glenn, Jim, *Scientific Genius: The Twenty Greatest Minds*, Crescent Books, New York, 1996

Grant, John, and Ray Jones, *Legendary Lighthouses* (The Companion to the PBS Television Series), The Globe Pequot Press, Old Saybrook, Conn., 1998.

Hague, Douglas B., and Rosemary Christie, *Lighthouses: Their Architecture, History and Archaeology*, Gomer Press, Llandysul, Wales, 1975.

"History of the Coastwise Lights of Lancashire and Cheshire," *The Compass, A Magazine of the Sea*, Vol. XLV, No. 3, 1975.

Holland, F. Ross, *America's Lighthouses: An Illustrated History*, Dover Publications, Mineola, New York, 1988.

———, *Great American Lighthouses*, Preservation Press, Washington, D.C., 1994.

———, *Lighthouses*, Metro Books, New York, 1995.

———, *Maryland Lighthouses of the Chesapeake Bay*, Maryland Historical Trust, Crownsville, 1997.

The International Association of Marine Aids to Navigation and Lighthouse Authorities, *Lighthouses of the World*, The Globe Pequot Press, Old Saybrook, Conn., 1998.

Jones, Ray, and Bruce Roberts, *American Lighthouses: A Comprehensive Guide*, The Globe Pequot Press, Old Saybrook, Conn., 1998.

———, *Northern Lighthouses: New Brunswick to the Jersey Shore*, 2nd ed, The Globe Pequot Press, Old Saybrook, Conn., 1994

———, *Pacific Northwest Lighthouses: Oregon, Washington, Alaska, and British Columbia*, The Globe Pequot Press, Old Saybrook, Conn., 1993.

Kausche, D., H. Ramm, and E. v. Lehe, *Heimatchronik der Freien und Hansestadt Hamburg*, Archiv für deutsche Heimatpflege GmbH, Köln, 1967.

Lyons, Walter A., Ph.D, *The Handy Weather Answer Book.* Visible Ink Press, 1997.

Mahan, Alfred Thayer, *The Influence of Sea Power upon History, 1660–1805*, Gallery Books, New York, 1980.

Maine Scene, Inc., *Lighthouses of Maine: A Pictorial Guide*, Union, Maine, 1995.

Naish, John, *Seamarks: Their History and Development*, Stanford Maritime Ltd., London, 1965.

Nicholson, Christopher, *Rock Lighthouses of Britain: The End of an Era?*, Whittles Publishing, Caithness, Scotland, 1995.

Nordhoff, Charles, *The Light-Houses of the United States in 1874* (facsimile ed.), Vistabooks Publishing, Silverthorne, Colo., 1993.

Oleszewski, Wes, and Wayne S. Sapulski, *Great Lakes Lighthouses, American & Canadian,* Avery Color Studios, Gwinn, Mich., 1998.

Olsen, H., and B. Studt, *Hamburgische Geschichte,* Verlag C. Boysen, Hamburg, 1929.

Peeters, Judith, *Changing Coastlines,* New Holland (Publishers) Ltd., London, 1998.

Philip's Geographic Encyclopedia of the World, Chancellor Press, London, 1988.

Porter, John, *History of the Fylde of Lancashire,* original archive, Lancashire, England.

Pringle, Patrick, *Jolly Roger: The Story of the Great Age of Piracy,* W.W. Norton, New York, 1953.

Quayle, Louise, *Weather: Understanding the Forces of Nature,* Crescent Books, New York, 1990.

Rothwell, Catherine, *Fleetwood Lighthouses and A History of Fleetwood-on-Wyre, 1834–1934* (Copyright Library Association and author, Fleetwood-on-Wyre, England, n.d.).

Simpson, Capt. Alex, *A Sailor's Guide to Wind, Waves and Tides,* Waterline Books, Shrewsbury, 1996.

Snow, Edward R., *Famous Lighthouses of New England,* Yankee Publishing, Boston, 1945.

Stephens, Dave, and Susan Rangles, *Discover Prince Edward Island: Adventure and Lighthouse Guide,* Nimbus Publishing, Halifax, Nova Scotia, 1999.

Stephens, Dave, *Discover Nova Scotia Lighthouses,* Nimbus Publishing, Halifax, Nova Scotia, 1998.

Thompson, William O., *Lighthouse Legends and Hauntings,* Scapes Me Publishing, Kennebunk, Maine, 1993.

Watson, Bruce, "Science Makes a Better Lighthouse Lens," *Smithsonian,* Aug. 1999, Vol. 30, No. 5.

Witney, Dudley, *The Lighthouse,* New York Graphic Society, Boston, 1975.

Additional information obtained from Encyclopedia Britannica Online, the U.S. Coast Guard, and the National Park Service's Maritime Initiative.

INDEX

Page numbers in *italics* refer to illustrations.

ACKNOWLEDGMENTS, PHOTO & ART CREDITS

ACKNOWLEDGMENTS

The publisher would like to thank the following individuals for their help in the preparation of this book: Sara Hunt, editor; Robin Langley Sommer, associate editor and contributor; Nicola J. Gillies, photo editor; Charles J. Ziga, art director and photographer; Nikki L. Fesak, graphic designer and photographer; Glenn O. Myers, consultant, technical artist and contributor; Clare Haworth-Maden, indexer; James P. Rodey, III, artist. The input of the following people was invaluable: Amanda L. Blattner, WBAL-TV/RADIO; Ed and Debby Cooper; Anthony Coviello; Lisa Langone Desautels; Bob Drapala; Skip Gardella, marine engineer; Tim Harrison, *The Lighthouse Digest*; James Hyland, The Lighthouse Preservation Society; Peter Grimm, NOAA Environmental Information Services; Peter M. Manjuck, Patti Morcos and Wayne A. DiGiacomo of Champion Printing; Joe McCary, Photo Response; Carol Morgan, Institute of Civil Engineers, London; Lorraine Myers; Barbara Taub, Alphapix; Ken Tretheway, The Lighthouse Society of Great Britain.

The publisher is extremely grateful to the following contributors who lent their expertise to the book: John Gibson, J. Keith Hunt, James Hyland, Heinz Lindenberg, Dominic Mariani, Glenn O. Myers, Jem Smallwood, Robin Langley Sommer and Tom Tasselmyer.

Grateful acknowledgment is also made to the following individuals and organizations for their assistance on photo shoots: Cathy Dolan; Marilyn Holnsteiner; Chief Warrant Officer John Strausser of the USCG ANT Long Island Sound, Stratford Point Lighthouse; Chiefs Mike Jensen and Jim Teeter, and P.O.s Mike Bero, Tony Carnegie and Mike Presti of the USCG ANT Long Island Sound, Southwest Ledge Lighthouse; Tom Hoffmann, Park Historian, Navesink Twin Lights, New Jersey; Ms. Betty Muguier, Hereford Inlet Lighthouse, New Jersey; Bob Larosa and Tony Poldino, Fire Island Lighthouse, New York.

ART CREDITS

The publisher acknowledges the following individuals whose art is featured on the pages listed below:

© Nikki L. Fesak: 194; **© James P. Rodey, III:** 15, 17;
© Glenn O. Myers: 111, 160, 198, 199.

PHOTO CREDITS

Permission to reproduce photographs on the pages listed below was provided by:

© Peter Arnold, Inc.: 4 (© Helga Lade), 8–9 (© Helga Lade), 112t (© Jim Wark), 150b (© Auscape/Ferrero), 188 (© Jim Wark); **© Tony Arruza:** 27, 155b; **© Mary Liz Austin:** 43, 123, 152–54; **© Barrett & McKay Photo:** 46, 54, 58, 70, 103, 105, 150t, 158; **© Nancy Hoyt Belcher:** 66, 116, 146, 167b; **© Cheryl Hogue/Britstock:** 31, 42b; **© Kindra Clineff:** 130, 140–41b; **© Kathleen Norris Cook:** 85t; **© Ed Cooper Photo:** 142–43; **© D.E. Cox Photo Library:** 64–65; **© Cameron Davidson:** 29; **© Grace Davies:** 109; **© Terry Donnelly Photo:** 22–23, 47, 48–49, 50, 59, 98–99, 106–107, 144, 151; **© Robert Drapala:** 53, 108, 120; **© Nikki L. Fesak:** 3, 78 (all), 79, 82 (all), 83, 137, 164 (all), 165, 172, 186, 187b; **© A. Blake Gardner:** 2, 25, 33, 156; **© 1989 Jean Guichard, Alphapix:** 40, 110, 112b; **© Thomas Hallstein/Outsight:** 39 (both); **© Rudi Holnsteiner:** 71, 94–95, 97, 100t, 102, 181, 183; **© Dave G. Houser:** 32, 34t, 51, 95 (© Dave G. Houser), 117t; **© James Hyland:** 117t, 133, 136, 139t, 173, 175b; **© Wolfgang Kaehler:** 34b, 42t, 56, 69, 85b, 88, 89, 113b, 149; **© Glenn O. Myers:** 160; **© Panos Pictures:** 139b (© Jean Léo Dugast); **© Chuck Pefley:** 35–37; **© Dusty Perin/Lady-Hawke Images:** 80–81, 90b; **© Chuck Place:** 38, 55, 145, 159; **© John Sylvester:** 41, 45, 74–75, 77, 84, 170; **© Graeme Teague:** 26, 100b, 166; **© Transparencies Inc.:** 52 (© Joe McLear), 57 (© Joe McLear); **© Stephen Trimble:** 12, 19, 161; **© Visuals Unlimited:** 67 (© Nada Pecnik), 155t (© Manfred Klindwurt), 189 (© Preston J. Garrison), 190 (© Barbara Gerlach); **© Charles J. Ziga:** 1, 44, 60–61, 62–63, 72 (all),73, 76, 86 (all), 87, 90t, 91, 92 (all), 93, 96, 104, 113t, 114, 117b, 121, 124, 125–28 (all), 129, 131–32, 134–35, 138, 140t, 148, 162, 163, 167t, 168–69, 171, 174, 175t, 176–77, 178 (all), 179, 180, 184, 185 (both), 191, 196; **Lancashire Library:** 119, 122; **Mountain High Maps:** 198, 199; **National Archives:** 115, 187 top and middle, 216; **Saraband Image Library:** 11, 147.

R43737

7 Day Loan

WITHDRAWN
FROM STOCK